MIRACLES
of
SCIENCE

By

ARTHUR I. BROWN, M.D., F.R.C.S.Ed.,

FUNDAMENTAL TRUTH PUBLISHERS

FINDLAY, OHIO

FOREWORD

The forty talks which constitute this volume have been delivered by transcription over various radio stations—several along the entire Pacific Coast, and also in Chicago where the two stations owned and operated by the Moody Bible Institute have recently carried the program, Miracles of Science.

The aim of this radio program is not merely an educational one. Behind every talk is the desire of the speaker to impress his hearers with the indisputable, scientific fact of a personal, omnipotent Creator-God, and to exalt the Person and work of the Lord Jesus Christ.

There are many people who think sincerely that believers in Christianity, while intellectually honest, have based their ideas on desire rather than on fact. It is the hope of the author that such an erroneous impression will be entirely dissipated as these discussions are studied. It will be seen by the unbiased and intelligent reader that we Christians accepting Creation are on very firm ground.

Our convictions are not founded on superstition or fancy but on the proven facts of scientific discovery. We assert unequivocally that Gen. 1:1 is absolute truth: "In the beginning God created." Taken at its face value it is impossible to reconcile this with the theory of evolution. Certainly, in the Bible there is no suggestion of any evolutionary process. On the contrary, hundreds of times we are directed to the marvelous creative power of God. His might and wisdom are infinite according to the Record.

What method He used in Creation is not disclosed, but now, with the discovery of atomic energy and the way to control it, it is easier to understand how God could, and probably did, make use of this tremendous power.

Briefly, we know that matter is made up of particles,—molecules, atoms, electrons, protons, neutrons, and other infinitely small bits of matter or electrical energy. It is known that matter can be converted into energy by ordinary combustion—releasing molecular energy, but leaving the atoms unchanged. What has now happened is this. Countless millions of neutron bullets have been fired by a secret process, at an inconceivable speed of many thousands of miles per second, into the nucleus or core of the atom of Uranium 235, one of the isotopes of Uranium. The astonishing result has been that the enormous force which has held these infinitely tiny, atomic particles together has been conquered with the release of a power which fairly staggers the imagination. This force is irresistible, —annihilating, and disintegrating everything in its path. Man has been able, by God's permission, to enter the sacred precincts of His presence, and to discover one of His own weapons—atomic energy.

Scientists tell us that this same process is going on continually in the sun. The sun is the source of light and heat for our earth. We depend on it daily and the 19th Psalm suggests that the sun was created and "set" in its relation to earth precisely for that purpose. God planned it so. Its distance from the earth, its size, its degree of heat, the way it prevents its own destruction—all this and more were designed by the Creator. Certainly, viewing all these details, no intelligent person would attribute them to chance.

If the distance from the sun were materially increased or lessened, there would be no life on earth; if there were any considerable change in the size and heating power of the sun, death to everything would be inevitable. The only explanation is creation. In all these details we see design. If there is design, obviously, there must be a Designer.

The sun is destroying itself at the rate of 250,000,000 tons of matter every minute of time and has been doing this for thousands, or millions or, the scientists say, for billions of years. Why is the sun still in the heavens? Why has it not dissipated itself? And the answer seems to be in atomic energy with its power not only of destruction but of creation. Matter is constantly being converted into energy by this solar combustion, and just as constantly energy is being changed into matter,—so that Creation goes on simultaneously with destruction.

In this astonishing process we see God at work on a material universe,—mysteriously using His wisdom and omnipotence. But there is a far greater miracle to which our attention is drawn repeatedly in God's Word. It is mentioned many, many times. For instance, listen to 2 Cor. 5:17: "Wherefore if any man be in Christ, he is a new creature (R. V. There is a new creation.): the old things are passed away; behold, they are become new."

This is the Good News of salvation, and to the dissemination of that Gospel, this book is dedicated. May the blessed Holy Spirit use each discussion to bring every reader into a new consciousness of the reality and saving power of the Lord Jesus Christ. What a Saviour—and never forget—HE'S WONDERFUL!

CONTENTS

CHAPTER I

THE HONEY-BEE AT WORK

Today I shall discuss the Honey-bee including the wonders of the Bees' knees. Honey-bees have been on earth for thousands of years and as far as we know are today exactly what they were from the beginning. They continue, now as always, to excite the **greatest** degree of admiration and interest, intriguing the human mind with the marvels of their structure, and even more, with the intricacy of their mysterious operations. As our talks continue, we shall examine some of these. For the moment let us glance briefly at the mechanical equipment on the knees of the three pairs of legs possessed by this astonishing insect.

You have, doubtless, noticed the two rodlike projections extending out in front of the bee and constantly on the move. It used to be thought that these were "feelers" but now it is known that they are "smellers" —in fact, the nose of the bee. Apparently, every bee has its own distinctive odor, which characteristic serves admirably as a means of identification among the hive members.

Accordingly, it is necessary that the sense of smell be acute, and that the apparatus be kept in perfect functioning condition. On the tips of these two antennae are thousands of tiny sense-plates—2,000 to 30,000 —the queen having the least and the drones the most. The drones need to be able to follow the queen on their nuptial flight—and they do so, not by sight so much as by odor.

These sense-plates are constantly rubbing against pollen dust as the bee inserts her head into the nectar-holding flowers; and occasionally they become coated with propolis or bee-glue. There must be some special appliance then for cleaning and that is exactly what she has. The device resembles a self-threading needle. On the front pair of legs is a movable piece of horn-like tissue, which can be raised by the bee, making a small opening, on the outer side of which are stakes or teeth—really stiff hairs which serve a very useful purpose. Let us suppose she desires to clean her right antenna. She bends it to the left, lifts the horny piece— the gate—inserts her antenna, drops the gate, and then draws the smeller back and forth between the stiff hairs placed outside the gate, until all dirt and dust be removed. When the same operation is performed on the other side, the tool is again functioning perfectly.

On the middle pair of legs at the knee joint is a short projecting spur, like a diminutive crow-bar or elephant's tusk, a very useful tool, needed especially for packing pollen dust into the pollen-basket which is a curious hollow depression on the flat, outer surface of the hind leg. On the inner part of this hind leg are a series of side-combs; these combs are constantly being applied to the hairy body of the bee in order to gather the pollen dust which is then dropped or scraped into the pollen basket and packed tight by the crow-bar.

The bee's life depends on the efficiency of these devices. There could not possibly have been a time when they did not possess them; otherwise they could not have survived, and these appliances could not develop gradually through long periods of time from a small beginning. They must have been created as we see them today. Chance could not produce these exact and efficiently functioning tools. Here is the designing Mind of a Supreme Being.

The Bible tells us to study these amazing insect creatures and to learn from them. This we shall try to do on many future occasions.

But now, let us turn for a few moments to another wonderful product of divine Wisdom. I refer to the Bible. May I offer some general comments on this great and miraculous Book—a true scientific Miracle?

The Bible is a Book which speaks of everything, describes nature, proclaims its grandeur, and tells the story of creation. It informs us of the structure of the heavens, of the creation of light, waters, atmosphere, mountains, animals and plants. It speaks of things visible, and at the same time, speaks of things invisible, and takes us into the realm of the celestial world.

It is the product of many writers of many degrees of mental cultivation, separated by 1,500 years from one another. It is written in the center of Asia, among the sands of Arabia and in the rustic schools of the prophets of Bethel and Jericho. Parts of it originate in the sumptuous palaces of Babylon, on the idolatrous banks of the River Chebar, and afterwards at the center of civilization, amid pantheism, polytheism and infidel philosophy.

Yet, in not a single sentence does it oppose the latest discoveries of science in any field of scientific investigation. As Henry Rogers once said: "The Bible is a book which man could not have written if he would, and would not have written if he could.

It is not a Book of speculations and guesses, representing the groping of the human mind after God. It is a Revelation, the discovery God has made of Himself to mankind. It is the Statute-Book of the human race.

To look at it, it is a Book of scraps, a planless cluster of pamphlets, representing the literature of the most unliterary of nations—66 booklets most diverse in character, scattered thinly over 16 centuries. They are made up of biographies, hymns, episodes of tribal history, laws of a social system which no longer exists, letters to churches dead for centuries, tales of old, far-off and forgotten things and battles of long ago.

One Book is an eastern love story; another is an episode in Persian history which has not in it once the name of God; yet another is a letter carried by an escaped slave who is being sent back to his master. This amazing Book affronts all expectation, and seems in its literary form, entirely unfitted for the great offices of a Bible, yet it has influenced the history of the race and the imagination of the world, not only more than any other book which can be named, but more than all books put together. It has determined the morality of the race. Nations LIVE by it, or die by quarreling with it. This tiny collection of Hebrew books not only lies on every pulpit lid in Christendom, but it is the shaping force in human affairs everywhere.

Generation after generation arises, each with its separate ideals and deeds, each with its own language. The literature of yesterday is not the literature of today. Famous books go out of fashion and are read only by scholars and antiquarians, but this immortal Book is the contemporary of all the ages. It talks with the accents of each generation in turn. The silver cord of the Bible is not loosed nor its golden bowl broken as centuries slip by like beads on the thread of time.

History is strewn with the wrecks of a hundred perished literatures, but time has no destroying office for biblical records. Some element not born of human genius lies in its pages, and outshines genius. This Book belongs to all the centuries and outlives them all.

One sublime idea shines behind the many books of the Bible. This idea is the recovery of a fallen race, and the great instrument of this process is the Lord Jesus Christ. The Bible is a portrait. The face of Christ looks out—tender, pure, divine—from every page. Is it credible that 66 chance daubs, of chance colors, made without any agreement among themselves by a number of chance men, could possibly produce a face which not only arrests the attention, but stirs the love of the world? No! There must be a single controlling Mind behind the brush of the Artist. No one can pretend that a handful of untaught Jews, herdsmen, fishermen, peasants, could outscale in intellectual, literary power, all the great minds not only of Greek and Latin literature, but of the literature of all races and all ages.

To take the personal and intellectual element in the writers and to try to explain the Bible by them is like taking the dead wire, the metal switch, the loop of calcined fibres, and offering them as an explanation of the electric light, itself. These things are but the channel of that subtle, invisible force, running back into mystery that we call electricity.

When any one can explain the electric light without an electric current, then we may explain the Bible without a divine inspiration. Something is in the Book which breaks out, now in one place, now in another, with pulses of spiritual energy, gleams of unearthly light. It is flooded from cover to cover with inspiration. It is as though at first one cluster of words and then another become suddenly and strangely luminous. For the devout soul, the Bible is always a Book of divinest magic.

As you have scanned the pages, have you seen the face of the Man of Galilee—the wonderful Saviour of the world? Has He come into your life? If not, why not give Him a chance to do what you cannot do for yourself? All He requires is to be invited. Will you do it today? It would be an intelligent and logical decision to make.

CHAPTER II

THE HONEY-BEE AT WORK

For thousands of years man has gazed on the Honey-bee with awe and wonderment. This tiny bit of animated protoplasm possesses a mysterious power which enables it to perform the most intricate and complex physiological operations and, by amazing industry, to accomplish remarkable feats of hive construction. The wax material for its home is manufactured in its own body. The bee exhibits more than human skill in producing honey from the watery fluid she finds in the heart of flowers. Then, having effected this magic change, she makes a gift of it to mankind.

Many centuries ago, honey was the main sugar supply of the world. As early as 3,500 B. C. Egyptian monuments portrayed the honey-bee as an honored member of the community, supplying ample quantities of this delightful product, which sold at about five cents a quart.

Bees ask few favors of mankind except that of non-interference. They are brave and self-reliant, dying at the post of duty, literally of physical exhaustion, worn out by their strenuous labors. The active life of the worker bee is only about 35 or 40 days. Man may kill the bee, but he cannot conquer it.

The bee is almost the only domesticated insect among the 600,000 insect species. The honey produced annually is worth millions of dollars; and the value of bees to orchardists, whose plants are pollenized, is incalculable.

In all its varied forms the bee is guided by instinct. Its short life permits but scant time for learning. In a very few days after hatching from the larval stage, we find bees gathering honey and taking part in all the active operations of the hive. This work would seem to require a knowledge of chemistry, architecture and other arts, which man learns slowly and laboriously. It begins life fully provided with everything needed to carry out the diversified jobs allotted to it. The only explanation that seems possible is CREATION.

The art of manufacturing honey is the sole prerogative of bees. They have a long, hollow tongue, which is a suckling tube able to reach the deepest part of the flower and extract the tiny drop of nectar. This is repeated from flower to flower until the honey bag or crop is full. Then the chemical factory within the body begins to function. From the salivary glands in the mouth, complex organic substances, known as enzymes, are poured out and mixed with the nectar. As the bee flies home, the sugar of the nectar is being changed into the dextrose and levulose of honey.

At the hive, the load of nectar is passed on to the crops of the younger workers who are acting as nurses for the 1,000 to 1,500 bee babies born daily. These nurse bees force the fluid in and out through their bodies in a thorough mixing process until a thin honey is formed which contains considerable water. This thin honey is emptied into the cells, which are not capped until sufficient water has evaporated, and it has the proper consistency.

We can appreciate the prodigious labor involved in honey making, when we know that it takes about 37,000 loads of nectar to make one pound of honey and that the workers from one hive—say, 35,000 to

50,000—will visit more than a quarter of a million blossoms in a single day, gathering this amount. To collect a pound of honey, even where flowers are plentiful, requires a flight mileage of 50,000 miles—equal to two circuits of the globe.

The bee has two pairs of amazingly efficient and powerful wings. They give evidence of special designing. The larger front wing has on its rear edge a ridge. To this ridge, hooks on the front edge of the back wing are fastened when flying. This device converts the four wings into two large ones for flight. Otherwise they would be too big to fit the small six-sided cells into which the bee must enter, so, at rest, the wings overlap beautifully and easily, thus reducing their size. No chance about this.

The wings beat 190 times a second or 11,400 times a minute, moving in a figure-of-eight design which makes possible flight in any direction—up, down, side to side, backward and forward; and as we have seen many times, the bee can poise motionless while hovering over a flower. The wings are very powerful so that the bee can lift loads much heavier than itself and fly at an estimated speed of about 15 miles an hour with apparent ease.

Yes, these are Miracles of Science, but may I bring to you again some thoughts about that other Miracle— the product of the wisdom of the divine Author— known as the Word of God?

The Apostle Paul was a great scholar and one of the keenest intellectuals who ever walked the world's stage. He wrote long ago to some friends in Thessalonica, and we read in his first letter to the Thessalonians, chapter 2, verse 13:

> "We also thank God without ceasing that
> when ye received from us the word of the
> message, even the Word of God, ye ac-
> cepted it not as the word of man, but, as it
> is in truth, the Word of God."

The conditions under which the Book was written convince the reader of its divine inspiration. It was produced by men ranking from peasants to kings; yet one unified theme of worship is found throughout its pages.

With hundreds of conflicting pagan cults and heathen practices surrounding the divine penmen as they wrote the 66 books, during the fifteen centuries covered by its writing, its divinity is undefiled. One voice speaks from all the records of Holy Scripture.

Where did the writers of the Bible get such conceptions of the one God while the foremost nations were worshipping idols, while Egypt bowed to the crocodile, and Athens gave 60,000 women to the terrible rites of Venus, while Rome was adoring the bloody God of war, while even the Parsi got no higher than to turn his face eastward and adore the sun? Who guarded the Scriptures from the pagan influences and fanciful philosophies of that day?

Few things are more arresting than the marvelous way in which certain brief statements in this Book have won the hearts of all kinds and conditions of men. I am thinking of John 3:16 and the world-shaking pronouncement of Jesus Christ:

> "For God so loved the world that He gave
> His only begotten Son, that whosoever be-
> lieveth in Him should not perish but have
> everlasting life."

Peasants and kings, statesmen and beggars, the self-righteous saint and the God-defying sinner, the child at mother's knee, and the aged about to step into eternity, the ignorant and untaught, the wise and the learned, the rich man and the poor man, have all heard the music of this heavenly pronouncement. They have believed it, trusted it, and been saved by it.

Egerton Young, the great missionary to the Indians, tells how he once invaded the Nelson River district and opened work among the people who had never before heard the Gospel. As he tells the story of how he was surrounded by 250 or 300 Indians—wild and war-like savages—he says, "I read aloud the sublime word: 'For God so loved the world that He gave His only begotten Son that whosoever believeth in Him should not perish but have everlasting life.' They listened with rapt attention as through four hours I talked to them of the truths of this glorious verse. When I had finished, every eye turned towards the chief. He rose, and coming near me, delivered one of the most thrilling addresses I have ever heard.

" 'Missionary,' exclaimed the stately old chief, 'I have not for a long time believed in our religion. I hear God in the thunder, in the tempest, and in the storm. I see His power in the lightning that shivers the trees. I see His goodness in giving us the moose, the reindeer, the beaver and the bear. I see His loving-kindness in sending, when the south winds blow, the ducks and the geese; and when the ice and snow melt away and our lakes and rivers are open again, I see how He fills them with fish. I have watched all this for years, and I have felt that the Great Spirit, so kind and watchful and loving, could not be pleased with the beating of the drum or the shaking of the rattle by the medicine man, and so I have had no religion, but what you have just said fills my heart with joy and satisfies its longings. I am so glad you have come with this wonderful story. Henceforth this Jesus is my God and this poor Indian is His.' "

That was a great decision for an Indian chief and a wise one. What are you going to do about this question?

CHAPTER III

THE HONEY-BEE AT WORK

In previous messages we have considered briefly some of the strange mechanical equipment of the honey-bee, as well as the process by which honey is manufactured by these skilled chemists. In addition to honey, the bee's mind—if we think of it as having a mind—is intent on two other things—pollen-dust or flour, and propolis or bee-glue.

The pollen, gathered daily by the bees as they enter and leave the flowers, is literally gold-dust to them. Rich in protein, it is fed to the workers in the summer colony. The fertilization of plants depends principally on the work of these busy bees; and if they were to be destroyed, there would be famine in the land, so the omniscient Creator, with great wisdom, has planned that these tiny insects should be indispensable to mankind.

Propolis, the dark colored bee-glue with which they fill cracks and smooth over rough places within the hive, is gathered from the gums of buds, plants, and trees. It is a most effective varnish, and yet the bee never seems to have any difficulty in preventing itself from becoming "stuck up" with it.

Another product of the chemical factory of the bee is wax. This very interesting material, so essential to hive making, is manufactured from its body after it has gorged itself with honey. Six or seven pounds of honey are required to make one pound of wax.

After a series of exact preparations by the inmates of the hive, the purpose of which seems to be to generate sufficient heat, as their movements reach a vigorous stage, the wax, secreted from four tiny factories on each side of the abdomen, appears as small thin flakes looking like fish-scales.

Each scale is removed by the hind pair of legs, carefully transferred to the middle pair, then to the mouth where it is mixed with saliva and changed from its first transparent form to the pale yellow color of the finished article.

Bees' wax is unlike anything else in the world. It contains a fatty acid called cerin, minute quantities of alcohol, myricin, hydro-carbons, and another acid which gives the wax its characteristic odor. It floats on water and is very resistant to heat, enduring a temperature of 140 degrees F. before melting. No other wax has such a high melting point.

The reason for this is easily discerned. The entire store of liquid gold would be lost if the thin-walled treasure vaults, the storage chambers, softened under the influence of moderate heat and gave way.

In manipulating the wax, in order to form the marvelous six-sided cells, real mechanical engineering skill is apparent. Without any chief engineer to issue commands, one piece of wax and then another is laid down by the busy workers, a tap here, a dab there, and presently a cell takes shape. What is the explanation of the ability to perform these precise and intricate operations? If it be that "spirit of the hive" mentioned by Maeterlinck, is that spirit not the Spirit of God? Certainly, it cannot be accounted for by thinking that the bee has gradually evolved this skill. If there ever was a time when it did not possess this knowledge, all bees would have died. The first bees, then, must have known how to do these things. That means creation, not evolution.

Yes, there are many inexplicable wonders wrapped up in the structure and work of the honey-bee. We find it difficult to explain these wonders without accepting the idea that God made it possible for these tiny life forms to acquit themselves so admirably in the struggle for existence.

To an even greater degree we find ourselves faced with an unsolvable dilemma if we attempt to explain the Bible without a supernatural God as Author. The qualifications of the human scribes, who produced the 66 books making up the Bible, are wholly inadequate to explain what we find in the pages of this remarkable Volume.

Here is a Book which is the greatest literary possession of the race, the enduring Revelation of God to man. It constitutes the title-deed to human institutions. It is the lesson-book of Christian faith, the final code of human conduct. Man, unaided, simply could not originate it.

If asked to describe in advance what the Bible of the human race should be, certainly no one would have guessed this particular form. It would be natural to ask if we might not have a book with fewer mysteries and digressions, a book that leaves nothing untold, a book which might be demonstrated like a problem in Euclid, a book which Higher Critics could not dissolve into a thin mist of wavering dates. A Revelation given to all, given simultaneously, and adequately, seems to be what is needed.

Well, let us imagine a committee of philosophers, poets, lawyers, historians, or newspaper writers, employed to draw up in advance a plan for the Bible. It is highly probable that such a committee would never have agreed among themselves, but it is certain that, if they had, they would have given us a Bible quite unlike the one it has pleased God to bestow.

The lawyers would have given us a code; the theologians a catechism. The committee of newspaper editors would have provided us with an up-to-date book, all headlines, sensation, and picturesque descriptions. The poets would have given us an epic embroidered with sonnets. The scientists would have made science itself unnecessary by preparing a compendium of all knowledge, the natural history of things in general, a book which would have left the planet without a secret, and the human intellect with nothing to interest it.

Uninspired human literature presents many differences from this great Book. For instance, Hodder's "Life of the Earl of Shaftesbury" contains some 360,000 words. Mr. Morley writes "The Life of Gladstone" on a still ampler scale in two stupendous volumes.

But for the Life of Christ, we have four thin pamphlets not much larger than tracts. Matthew tells the amazing story in 23,000 words, while Mark requires only 15,000 words.

In spite of innumerable attempts at destruction, the Book lives on. Henry Rogers wrote that "The little ark of Jewish literature floats upon the surges of time, while the wrecked archives of huge oriental empires are turned into mere flotsam and jetsam."

How often has the Bible been torn into rags, refuted and destroyed! But, the anvil outlasts all the hammers that smite it. The men who attack the Bible, the volumes written to disprove it, are forgotten, while the immortal Book lives on, surviving its friends as well as its enemies.

Some strange gift of indestructible life is hidden in this volume. History is strewn with the wrecks of a hundred perished literatures, but time has no destroying office for Biblical records.

Some element, not born of human genius, lies in its pages, and outshines genius. Other books have their day and die. Their language grows obsolete. The world's thought runs in new channels, and they are left mere stranded wrecks on Time's shore, but this Book belongs to all the centuries and outlives them all.

One sublime idea shines behind the many books of the Bible. This idea is the recovery of a fallen race, and the instrument of this great process is the Lord Jesus Christ. The Bible is nothing but a frame of historical events in which the face of Christ is set. All the early books of the Bible prepare for Him, point to Him, all the later books look back to Him. Under all its forms the Bible is thus the servant of but one idea.

Or, to vary the figure, the Bible is a portrait. The face of Christ looks out, tender, pure, divine,—it may be, with varying clearness, but from every page. Is it credible that sixty-two chance daubs of chance colors, made without any agreement among themselves by a number of chance men, could possibly produce a face that not only arrests the attention but stirs the love of the world?

Tried by ordinary tests, the Bible is thus the great puzzle of all literature. What is the explanation of the puzzle? The only answer is that the Bible is not the product of human genius. It does not reflect the mind nor record the discoveries of man. It reflects the mind of God. It is a channel through which runs a stream of spiritual force. It is not a discovery but a Revelation.

The Bible does not argue. It pronounces. It is not concerned to prove by argument the foundations of religion, the existence and holiness of God, the eternal authority of righteousness, the moral nature of man, the fact of sin, and of redemption from the guilt and power of sin, and that final judgment that awaits all human deeds.

It assumes these truths and proclaims them as certainties that find their attestation in the soul, itself. The Bible offers us, not an argument, but a message. It is not man's thoughts about God, but God's thoughts about man. So the note is always one of authority— an authority which cannot be assailed nor challenged because it is final and absolute. GOD HAS SPOKEN.

In view of this great Revelation, it surely is worth while to pay attention to the advice given humanity in the Bible. The message it delivers is concerned with the problem of making a way of escape for all of us sinners from the penalty of sin which is death. "The soul that sinneth, it shall die" ends all discussion. But here God steps in and offers a remedy—a Divine Substitute for us in the Person of His Son, who died for us "in our room and stead." God requires one thing only—that we link ourselves up with this Son—the blessed Man of Galilee. To refuse means eternal punishment; but to accept means eternal life. Who would choose the former when the consequences are known? Will you take Jesus NOW?

CHAPTER IV

BABY BEES AND THEIR NURSES

For the benefit of those who may be listening for the first time to this broadcast, let me say that we have been considering some of the marvels of the Honey-Bee, one of the most interesting forms of life. We have discovered its many mysterious powers and have drawn attention to its unique mechanical equipment of strange tools, exquisitely adapted to its varied needs. We have found no answer for these except in the fact of creation by an all-wise God. A gradually evolving instinct would be impossible. That would indicate that there was a time when these powers were non-existent or very immature, but when we remember that the life of these insects depends on the possession of a perfect instinct, necessary to insure their propagation and perpetuation, there could never have been a period when they were not equipped as they are now. The only explanation available is that a Creator endowed them thus at the very beginning.

From 1,000 to 1,500 bee babies are born daily to replace about an equal number of deaths. The feeding of these helpless life-forms presents to observers a most interesting phenomenon. A section of the hive is always set apart as the nursery and it is here that the Queen, in her daily rounds, lays the tiny eggs in specially prepared cells. These eggs hatch at the end of three days and we see a host of small white worms or grubs lying curled up and fitting accurately and snugly into their six-sided rooms.

Obviously, nurses are required and this work is carried out by the newly-born members of the colony who exhibit the most solicitous care for their young family. During the first 48 hours every bee baby is fed on what is known as royal jelly, a magic food manufactured in the ductless glands of the nurses, who seem to be constantly engaged in urging their proteges to eat. 300 meals a day are the approximate number of feedings given these rapidly growing children of the hive. The young bees lie literally surrounded by this jelly which is kept replenished from the mouths of the attendants, leaning over the edge of the cribs.

If a grub, born from an egg, fertilized by the Queen with a male sperm cell, were fed continuously during the five-day larval period, on royal jelly, it would develop into a Queen with fully-formed female reproductive organs. This is not required, except under special conditions, as when the Queen is getting too old for her work of egg-laying, or if she dies. Consequently, except when a Queen is wanted, the royal jelly diet ceases at the end of 48 hours, and is replaced by a mixture of honey and pollen dust, the proportions of each ingredient being very carefully measured by the expert nurses, who seem to be skilled chemists. Many experiments have shown that this food is mixed in exact proportions. Here is another instance of surprising and mysterious knowledge.

This change in the food results in the birth of neutral female bees—the workers with which we are so familiar. They perform most of the wonders of the hive and constitute the great mass of the bee population. How the royal jelly brings about the change from the neutral female state to a fully developed Queen is not known. It is the secret of the bee!

After five days of this intensive feeding, the tiny grub weaves for itself a silken shroud, having been equipped with this ability to produce silk just for this one stage of its existence. The silk factory is discarded in the next and final form. Here a question arises. How does it happen that there is present exactly when needed this silk factory inside the bee's body? The obvious design at this point suggests just one fact—a Designer or Creator.

After being surrounded by this silken covering for 12 or 14 days, there begins to stir into active life an entirely different body with wings and all the equipment, which has been described in previous talks. The nurses have capped over the cell where the hatching is taking place, and now this waxen cap is cut and there slowly emerges a somewhat bedraggled and apparently bewildered addition to the hive. The new member is granted about 24 hours to become familiar with its new surroundings. She wanders here and there, sniffing and inspecting, drying out her wings and developing the use of her legs and other body structures. Then she begins real work, entering the nursing section, without any instruction but also without any confusion or lack of skill. She proceeds to make royal jelly and feed her sisters who are coming into life just as she did a few hours before. Without benefit of teaching, she is able to perform all the duties of the community with unerring skill and with complete devotion to her lifework—a busy life while it lasts, but over in a month or six weeks.

Again we ask: Whence the astonishing wisdom displayed by this insignificant mass of protoplasm weighing only one five-thousandth of a pound—if not from God? May we not join with the Psalmist and say: Ps.

95:2, 3, "Let us come before his presence with thanksgiving, and make a joyful noise unto him with psalms. For the Lord is a great God and a great king above all gods."

The Bible speaks with no uncertain sound as to the Source of all these miracles which we are considering. In many ways, the Bible is the greatest miracle of all. We shall continue to stress the great truth that this is the Book of books, infallible in every part, because inspired in every word by its divine Author. Yes, verily, it is what William Ewart Gladstone called, "The impregnable Rock of Holy Scripture." On that Rock we take our stand.

It may be and probably is a fact that there are some listening now who do not quite agree with me as to this basic pronouncement, so let us give some thought to the question.

What are we to do with the Bible? How are we to regard it? Is it the best book in the world or is it the worst? Is it a true book or is it a false book? Is it God's Book or is it man's book?

We find men on all sides of the question. Some tell us this Book is a good book—but then, there are others just as good. They say the Bible is inspired but so were Plato and Socrates and so are many books, if not all. The Book of Mormon, the Koran of Mahomet, the sacred books of the Hindus and the Chinese—all are good and one is about as good as another. Shakespeare was inspired, Milton was inspired, Thomas Paine was inspired, everything and everybody is inspired.

But there seems to be a difference. When I open Shakespeare's plays, I do not read at the beginning: "Thus saith the Lord of hosts." When I turn to Plato's writings, I do not read: "Hear ye the Word of the Lord."

This book must be judged by standards different from those which apply to any other book. Either the message of this Book is the Word of God or it is a lie. It is what it claims to be, or it is a cheat, a swindle, a humbug, a fraud.

Someone tells me that Jesus of Nazareth was a good man; but then, he says, there were others just as good. What did Jesus say: "I came forth from the Father and am come into the world; again I leave the world and go to the Father." And also, I hear Him saying: "O Father, glorify Thou me with thine own self, with the glory which I had with Thee before the world was." Did He speak truth? If He did then He is on a different plane from any other man who ever lived. Do you say He was a good man and lied? I do not believe that a good man lies!

I do not believe that a book packed with lies from beginning to end is a good book; nor do I believe that Jesus Christ was a good man, and that the Bible is a good Book, if neither of them tells the truth. The Book is what it professes to be or it is a swindle. Jesus of Nazareth was what He professed to be or He was an impostor. We must accept His claims in their entirety, or else we must reject the whole Gospel as an imposture, and as the most stupendous fraud the world has ever known. There is no middle ground. Do not be fooled by this soft talk about the Bible being a good book, and yet just like many other books. There is not another like it in the world. Let us look again at some of its peculiarities.

The Bible is a book which has been refuted, demolished, overthrown and exploded more times than any other book of which you have ever heard. Every little while someone comes along and upsets it, but it is like upsetting a solid cube of granite. It is just as big one way as another, and when you have upset it, it is right side up, and when you turn it over again, it is still right side up.

Every little while someone blows up the Bible, but when it comes down, it always lights on its feet and runs farther than ever throughout the world. You remember, they overthrew it in Voltaire's time, about two centuries and a half ago. They were sure they had demolished the whole thing. "In less than 100 years," Voltaire sneered, "Christianity and the Bible will be swept out of existence and will have passed into history." Well, what happened? For a time, infidelity ran riot throughout France, red-handed and impious, but the centuries have gone into history now, and Voltaire is only a memory and not even a very respectable memory.

But listen, my friends, "The WORD OF GOD LIVETH AND ABIDETH FOREVER." How satisfying and how true are the words of the 119th Psalm, in the 89th verse, "Forever, O Lord, thy word is settled in heaven." I like that word, "settled." Nothing can disturb this magnificent Word of God. All the assaults of men and devils fall helpless and impotent against its impregnable walls. All the slanders and calumnies and false charges, prompted by hatred and distrust, do not disturb its calm dignified peace, nor send a quiver of fear into its breastplate of righteousness.

As for me, I shall link up with this blessed Book of God, I shall believe it when it tells me I am a sinner and Jesus Christ is my Saviour. I know the truth of both statements. Can you say as much today? Would it not be a good time now—yes, now—to bow in acknowledgment of your sin, knowing the penalty thereof is death, and accept the Saviour of sinners, the acceptance of Whom is Life Eternal? Will you do it?

CHAPTER V

THE BEES BUILD A MAUSOLEUM

Bees have a unique insect furnace which they use to keep the temperature of the hive comfortable even in the depth of winter when the thermometer registers 10 degrees below zero outside. The bees remain inside and are able to maintain their living quarters at 65 degrees F. If the air becomes heavy and there is need of ventilation, they know how to arrange themselves in proper formation and by vigorous action of their wings, one brigade on the inside and another on the outside, pull out the vitiated air and draw in clean, fresh supplies.

The way they dispose of the dead body of a mouse is interesting. This dead body will surely foul the entire hive, necessitating an abandonment of their home. How then can they get rid of the odor? They varnish the dead mouse from head to tail with propolis or beeglue, which forms an airtight mausoleum for the decomposing animal. Thus there is not the slightest contamination of their living abode.

These and many other wonders might well occupy our attention, but let us, as we take leave of the bee, make an early morning visit to a hive. The soft light of a new day is sweeping across the fields, and a stimulating breeze is moving among flowers, leaves, and shrubs.

Throughout the hive is the thrill of buoyant life. Thousands of workers buzzing about cause the beehouse to quiver with activity, but nowhere is there confusion; everything proceeds in orderly fashion. Each bee has its work to do and seems to do it joyously and with all its might.

The gatherers of nectar, led by scouts, fly in a "bee line" to the scene of action, making good time at about 15 miles an hour. Among the flowers still heavy with dew, they pass in and out, gathering pollen dust on their hairy covering, and using their slender curved tongues, like tiny scimitars, to draw from the blossoms the last drop of sweetness.

Then they fly back to the hive, pausing for a brief moment before the guards at the entrance, to give their peculiar salute and countersign, before entering to deposit their spoils. Here, in a little six-sided room with walls of solid wax, is the storehouse or bank of deposit. The records show that one colony of bees will yield from 50 to 100 pounds of the honey per season—very large return for their labor when we consider the insignificant amount each bee is able to manufacture in a day.

Honey is an admirable carbohydrate food. It consists of water, levulose, dextrose, cane sugar, dextrins, and gums, with very small quantities of ash, beeswax, a few pollen grains, and coloring material from the plants supplying nectar.

This delectable food contains substantial amounts of vitamins A, B, and C. None of these is found in highly refined cane or beet sugars. In addition, it contains carbohydrates, a small amount of protein, a generous quantity of the mineral salts, calcium, iron, iodine, copper and zinc, as well as enzymes and other vital and nutritional substances. Unlike table sugar, it is alkaline, hence does not tend to produce body acidity. It is the simplest and most digestible form of sweetening, and is readily absorbed and assimilated. In giving the Honey-bee to the world, the Creator has conferred a real blessing on humanity.

God has always been thoughtful of His creatures, and everywhere we see manifestations of His love and care. When He conferred on us the blessing of the Bible, this would seem to be the crowning evidence of His solicitude. Without this Book, we would know nothing about Him, and the astonishing program for the world which is laid out therein.

We have noticed how God's arch-enemy has attempted the destruction of the Holy Scriptures. Thomas Paine thought he had demolished the Bible, but after he had crawled despairingly into a dishonored grave, the Book took such a leap forward that the world's printing presses are almost unable to supply the enormous demand for millions of copies in more than a thousand languages and dialects.

Bob Ingersoll traveled around the country exploding the Book, and showing up the "Mistakes of Moses" at $200.00 a night. It is easy to abuse Moses at such a price, especially as Moses is dead and cannot talk back. It would be, I think, an exciting experience, after listening to an infidel speak on "The Mistakes of Moses," to hear Moses on, "The Mistakes of an Infidel"!

Moses, you know, was rather a difficult man to deal with. Pharaoh tried talking back to him, and met with rather poor success. Jannes and Jambres withstood Moses and found a grave in the Red Sea. Koran, Dathan, and Abiran tried it, but they went down so deep in the earth they have never returned. But now, Moses is dead and it is easy to abuse him. It does not take a very brave man to kick a dead lion!

What, then, makes this Book so different from all other books. Whose Book is it? Who made it? Infidels attribute the selection of the books, which comprise it, to the caprice of fallible and gullible men. Those who believe it are called ignorant and credulous.

But what does the Bible say about itself? Listen while it speaks. "Open thou mine eyes that I may behold wondrous things out of thy law." "Forever, O Lord, Thy word is settled in heaven." "Thy testimonies are wonderful, therefore doth my soul keep them." "The entrance of thy words giveth light; it giveth understanding to the simple." "Thy word is a lamp unto my feet, and a light unto my path." (Ps. 119.) "No prophecy of Scripture is of any private interpretation. For the prophecy came not in old time by the will of man; but holy men of God spake as they were moved by the Holy Spirit." (II Peter 1:21.)

Is this witness true? It must be. If that be so, then surely we are compelled to give our attention to the utterances of God, according them the honor and respect they command.

It was Dr. Van Dyke, I think, who expressed himself in words which ought to be remembered. He said:

> "Born in the East and clothed in oriental form and imagery, the Bible walks the ways of all the world with familiar feet and enters land after land to find its own everywhere. It has learned to speak in hundreds of languages to the heart of man. It comes into the palace to tell the monarch that he is a servant of the Most High and into the cottage to assure the peasant that

he is a son of God. Children listen to its
stories with wonder and delight, and wise
men ponder them as parables of life. It has
a word of peace for the time of peril, a
word of comfort for the time of calamity,
a word of light for the hour of darkness.
"Its oracles are repeated in the assembly of
the people, and its counsels whispered in
the ear of the lonely. The wicked and the
proud tremble at its warnings, but to the
wounded and penitent it has a mother's
voice. The wilderness and the solitary
place have been made glad by it, and the
fire on the hearth has lit the reading of its
well-worn pages. It has woven itself into
our dearest dreams, so that love, friend-
ship, sympathy, and devotion, memory and
hope put on the beautiful garments of its
treasured speech, breathing of frankin-
cense and myrrh."

Transcending all other benefits and blessings, we
find it the Way of Life. The Lord Jesus Christ is revealed as this Way, and also, the Truth, and the Life
itself. The Bible brings to us the only solution of the
world's need, and that solution is a Person, and that
Person, the Man of Galilee, the Son of God, God of
very God, dying for us on a cross raised high on Gol-
gatha's Hill.

Have you discovered and accepted this wonderful
and perfect Saviour? He waits for your answer. Make
it "Yes." You will, if you are wise. Then you can travel
life's road confident and unafraid. Whatever happens,
you will be sure that you are in His loving care.

"I will not doubt though all my ships at sea
Come drifting home with all broken masts
        and sails,
I will believe the hand which never fails,
From seeming evil, worketh good for me.
And though I weep because those sails are
        tattered,
Still I will cry while my best hopes are
        shattered—
'I trust in Thee.'
I will not doubt though all my prayers re-
        turn
Unanswered from the still white realm
        above.
I will believe it is an all-wise love
Which has refused these things for which I
        yearn;
And though at times I cannot keep from
        grieving,
Yet, the pure ardor of my fixed believing
Undimmed shall burn."

Precious, isn't He?

CHAPTER VI

THE WATER OF LIFE

The dictionary definition of water as a limpid liquid composed of hydrogen and oxygen is not very exciting news, but what a blessing to mankind it is, how indispensable to life, and how pleasure-giving as a luxurious beverage brewed for us by our heavenly Father! Yes, He brews it in grassy dells where the deer, the antelope, and the child love to play. He brews it on the mountain top whose granite peak glistens like gold in the sunlight. He brews it in the depths of the seas, and in subterranean caverns. You see it glistening in the dewdrop and singing in the summer rain. It sparkles in the ice gem when the trees seem as if loaded down with rare jewels. It gleams in the hoar-frost struck by the rays of the morning sun.

Hidden snugly in the depths of the evening clouds resting on the western horizon, God paints a gorgeous sunset shimmering with all the hues of heaven until our senses fairly reel with its beauty. This water of life brings refreshment and energy to man and beast and lowly plant. It is one of God's greatest gifts to the world. Water is responsible for the beauty of the rainbow, which is a circular spectrum. The spherical drops of water, falling out of the rain-cloud, become prisms by which rays of light are separated into their primary colors.

The component parts of water, as every one knows, are two gases—hydrogen and oxygen. Hydrogen is the most inflammable of gases, and oxygen is necessary for all fires. Yet, when these combine, they produce the best fire extinguisher known.

The action of low temperature on fluids is to increase their weight. This is true of water also until the temperature reaches within four degrees of freezing, when, instead of the specific gravity increasing, water becomes lighter and rises to the surface as ice is formed. The reason for this is not difficult to understand. If ice sank as soon as formed, all lakes and rivers would soon be solid and the result would be death to all their living inhabitants. So by changing an almost universal law, God removes from ice its death-dealing properties, so far as the fish are concerned, and causes it to act as a protective covering which keeps them warm during the months of severe cold. Certainly this does not appear to be simply due to chance.

Water in great quantities is constantly needed to sustain life in all the organic realms. No water, no life, is a basic law of the universe. There must be enough, but not too much. A mistake in either direction would be disastrous, so it is absolutely necessary that a definite and calculated amount should be available. In other words, if there is a Person in charge of these adjustments, we expect that He will in some way measure and prepare the right quantity.

To put it in another way, the earth's surface would have to be accurately apportioned as to land and water, and the ocean depths must be exactly the size to hold the necessary amount of liquid. There are 197,-000,000 square miles to the surface of the earth. What do we find? A most interesting phenomenon. There are 145,000,000 square miles of water and 52,000,000 square miles of land. This seems to us a strange proportion at first glance, but of course it is just what is needed by a thirsty earth with countless millions of inhabitants.

It is estimated that approximately 16,000,000 tons of water fall every second from the skies to the earth—truly a vast quantity. How this is lifted from earth to heaven, and then delivered to the earth, will be considered in subsequent talks, along with other miracles of water distribution. But it may be said at this point, and very forcibly, these requirements demand a Master Workman and Engineer!

What does the Bible have to say about water? In our next talk, we shall discover some remarkable scientific statements, hidden away in out-of-the-way places but full of meaning when the light of modern knowledge is focused upon them. That fact is one of the surprises this ancient Book brings to us. Unexpectedly it flashes upon our consciousness miraculous conceptions. They come, as it seems, from the pens of ignorant human writers. However, they are truths which, it may be, we have recently discovered, but have been handed down for thousands of years in this astonishing Library of super-natural origin.

One time in the long ago, Jesus carried on a conversation about water with a woman of Samaria, from whom He requested a drink of water when He sat near to Jacob's well, very weary after miles of walking in the hot Palestinian sun. But let the record speak for itself; the account is found in chapter 4 of John's Gospel.

"And He must needs pass through Samaria. So He cometh to a city of Samaria, called Sychar, near to the parcel of ground that Jacob gave to his son Joseph: and Jacob's well was there. Jesus therefore being wearied with His journey, sat as He was by the well."

Here is a picture of a tired Christ, seeking rest and dropping wearily to a seat — **as He was.** Note these strange words— "as He was." Mark uses them to describe His exhausted condition at another time when the disciples persuaded Him to lie down in the boat; "they took Him, as He was." Did the Son of God become completely fatigued? There can be no doubt about it. But let us continue the story.

"It was about the sixth hour. There cometh a woman of Samaria to draw water; Jesus saith unto her, Give me to drink. For his disciples were gone away into the city to buy food. The Samaritan woman therefore saith unto Him, How is it that thou being a Jew, askest drink of me, who am a Samaritan woman? Jesus answered and said unto her, If thou knewest the gift of God and who it is that saith unto thee, Give me to drink; thou wouldst have asked of him and he would have given thee living water.

"The woman saith unto him: Sir, thou hast nothing to draw with and the well is deep; whence then hast thou that living water? Art thou greater than our father Jacob who gave us the well, and drank thereof himself, and his sons and his cattle?

"Jesus answered and said unto her, Every one that drinketh of this water shall thirst again: but whoso drinketh of the water that I shall give him shall never thirst, but the water that I shall give him shall become in him a well of water springing up into everlasting life.

"The woman saith unto Him, Sir, give me this water that I thirst not, neither come all the way hither to draw."

This well known incident in the life of our Lord carries a great truth and many lessons.

A weary Christ, seeking physical refreshment from a woman of the world, took this trip for the purpose of bringing salvation to this obscure citizen of a Samaritan village. Yes, "He must needs go through Samaria." Why "must"? If He had not gone that way, this child of His would never have found the way home. She was lost in the wilderness of sin, but the Lord searched her out. He did a bit of personal work that day that has come down through the centuries to us, and wherever it is told, it brings blessing. It reveals God's interest in one insignificant person, and that individual **must** be saved. She was on God's list of children to be brought into vital contact with Jesus the Christ.

Her thirst would never have been satisfied by the sparkling water from Jacob's well. She would, Jesus said, thirst again, and she knew it. We must recognize her acute perception, her sharp intelligence as she took Him at His word, and quickly made her decision, "Sir, give me this water that I thirst not." She did not understand, but she believed He could do it.

And when she tasted, what did she do? She "left her waterpot," we read, and hurried back into the city without it. She had something better than a waterpot of H_2O. She had found Christ and eternal life, and so she called out, "Come, see a man . . . Can this be the Christ?"

From a water-carrier to thirsty Samaritans, who desired the physical satisfaction of water trickling over the tongue down the throat, she became a flaming evangelist. So that the record says, "And from that city, many of the Samaritans believed on Him because of the word of the woman who testified."

Friends, that was a real conversion. Do you know

anything about such an experience? Have you tasted the water of eternal life, handed out by the Saviour Jesus Christ? There is only one place where you can get it — from the nail-pierced hand of this wonderful Man of Galilee. It is free; it cannot be purchased; but you, personally, must seek it from the one and only original Source. You must ask for it and take it freely. "By grace are ye saved through faith, and that not of yourselves, it is the gift of God." And what a gift! Will you slake your thirst today at the fountain of living waters? You will find it to be the most satisfying drink you have ever known. Gloriously true it is, "Whosoever drinketh of the water that I shall give him shall never thirst." Eternal life for the taking! Will you have it?

CHAPTER VII

GOD'S PLAN FOR WATER DISTRIBUTION

Alfred Russell Wallace, one of the greatest scientists of the nineteenth century, and an eminent evolutionary authority, wrote a book—"Man's Place In the Universe," in which he pointed out a number of remarkable evidences of planning, in order that life might be possible on this planet.

There are five conditions essential to life. One of these is water in abundance and generally distributed. Obviously there must be a calculated amount, neither too much nor too little. In other words, it must be measured by the One who is in charge of this detail. Also, in order to hold this vast amount of water, there must be adequate basins or excavations in the earth itself.

In the third place, if millions of tons of water are falling out of the sky every second, this water must have been lifted previously into the upper atmosphere.

Another requirement is that the moisture must be distributed more or less evenly across the world, if a wide area is to be changed from arid desert to inhabitable land.

I suggest that here are several problems of supreme importance, presenting great difficulties in solution. The machinery, which makes these various operations possible, works smoothly, constantly and effectively. Does the Bible have anything to say about this? Now, I do not claim that the Bible is a scientific textbook, but rather, that whenever it touches a scientific question, it speaks with infallible authority.

What does the Bible say about the amount of water? In Isaiah 40:12, we read:

> "Who hath measured the waters in the hollow of his hand, and meted out heaven with a span, and comprehended the dust of the earth in a measure, and weighed the mountains in scales, and the hills in a balance?"

This verse, with its four amazing suggestions, has long been judged nothing more than picturesque language, without factual reality. When we give the matter a little thought, we see that God is directing skeptical human intelligence to notice a few of the adjustments without which would be no life on this globe. He is asking as to the source of the Power behind these adjustments. This entire chapter deals with the obvious evidences of His Personality and Wisdom, contrasted with the impotence of the idols held in such reverence by ignorant and thoughtless people.

Think of the first statement of this verse. "Who hath measured the waters in the hollow of his hand?" There can be no doubt that the Creator must have carefully planned the exact amount of water which covers such a great area of the earth. The words, "In the hollow of his hand," may be taken figuratively, if preferred, but it must have been necessary to calculate a definite quantity since a haphazard arrangement would have resulted in death. The method of measurement is not important. The fact is.

Next. How shall this water be held or retained in certain locations? If the earth were a round even ball, the water would run at random over its surface, thus making ordered life impossible. The only solution would seem to be excavations in the surface of the earth, deep enough and wide enough to hold the vast tonnage of liquid.

Hear this interesting statement in the 33rd Psalm and 7th verse. "He layeth up the deeps in storehouses." What a beautiful explanation! For that is just what the ocean depths are—storehouses. If they were too shallow, the plan would be defeated. If too deep, there would be difficulty because ships could not travel on the surface which would be far below the shore-lines. But this great Architect makes no mistakes. Men build storehouses for grain, which have a definitely measured capacity. Is it strange, then, that God should exercise forethought in this? The wonder is to have this explanation hidden away back in this Psalm, "He layeth up the deeps in storehouses"—a perfect figure of the Creator piling deep upon deep, laying it up in His basins of calculated capacity.

The third engineering problem concerns the job of lifting a fluid which is 800 times heavier than air, high into the atmosphere, holding it there and then causing it to fall in gentle showers on thirsty ground. How is the force of gravity to be defied and conquered, not once, but constantly, in order to raise 16,000,000 tons without apparent effort or disorder, each second? To man this would be impossible, but "with God all things are possible."

The 7th verse of Psalm 135 has three short clauses, crammed full of surprising scientific ideas — truths which were certainly not known or imagined when this Record was written. Let us read verses five, six and seven:

"For I know that the Lord is great, and that our Lord is above all gods.

"Whatsoever the Lord pleased, that hath
he done, in heaven and in earth, in the seas
and in all deeps; Who causeth the vapors
to ascend from the ends of the earth;
"Who maketh lightnings for the rain;
"Who bringeth forth the wind out of his
treasuries."

Let us glance also at another interesting and signif-
icant passage in the first chapter of Ecclesiastes, verses
six and seven.

"The wind goeth toward the south, and
turneth about unto the north; it turneth
about continually in its course, and the
wind returneth again according to its circuits. All the rivers run into the sea, yet
the sea is not full; unto the place from
whence the rivers come, thither they return again."

These are remarkable observations regarding puz-
zling phenomena — great quantities of water emptying into inland seas without any outlet, and yet the
water level in these seas remaining constant. The
question which arises intrigues us — What becomes of
the inflowing water? Why is the sea into which it
runs not "full" to overflowing?

The author of Ecclesiastes answers his own question by telling us an incredible thing, viz: the rivers
which came from the high places into the low, return
again to their first location on the heights.

We ask, "How can water, weighing 800 times more
than air, be raised against gravity miles above the
earth in hugh quantities daily?" The answer is found
in the first clause of this Psalm, "He causes the vapor

to ascend from the ends of the earth." That is, evaporation with all its amazing wonders is God's solution of this problem. And this answer to our question lies hidden in one of the Psalms, revealing very casually and without excitement the infinite wisdom of God, to whom all things are not only possible but easy.

What is evaporation? It is the strange effect of sunlight striking molecules of water and changing them instantly and noiselessly into molecules of watery vapor, in which form the new molecules occupy 1,600 times the space they did as water. That is, they are now water-vapor balloons, ascending on high in countless numbers each second of time, invisible to human vision and causing no disturbance of any kind. This is Deity in action.

If it was the Dead Sea which Solomon visited, he saw the torrential waters from the Jordan emptying their load daily into the Sea without any resulting overflow. This man, "under the sun," made a discovery thousands of years ago because he had asked that God give him wisdom. Only thus can we explain this altogether unexpected statement about evaporation, suggesting some sort of circular irrigation system of the world. Water reaches the hills and mountains, unites into rivers, tumbles into the Sea and then, mysteriously, causes no increase in the waters into which it is emptied. Stranger than all is the observation that the rivers, after their visit to the Sea, return again to their original place in the heights. Another impossible event according to human wisdom! Is there any wonder then when we read: "I know that the Lord is great, and that our Lord is above all gods."

What God are you worshiping today, my friend? Every one worships some one or something. Every one experiences both hunger and thirst. How are you endeavoring to meet these two needs? Is your food satisfying? Is your liquid nourishment really thirst-quenching?

You will agree with me that the man who knows not God is never satisfied as to hunger or thirst. There is only one food which nourishes and removes the pangs of spiritual hunger, and Jesus said, "I am the Bread of Life." You are hungry. Have you eaten of this Bread? The husks of the world bring no joy nor satisfaction. Why not try something else, that which thousands have tried and found to work?

You are thirsty. Your soul longs after that which will bring relief and you are drinking of what the world has to offer, partaking ceaselessly without relief. Remember what Jesus said: "Every one that drinketh of this water shall thirst again; but whosoever drinketh of the water that I shall give him shall never thirst."

What do you think about trying something new, which offers instantaneous and complete cure? If you had a bodily infirmity and had tried faithfully some suggested remedy which had absolutely failed, you would not continue the unsuccessful treatment indefinitely, would you? I offer you this infallible cure. The cure is a Person—the Lord Jesus Christ.

One drink from this Fountain of Living Water will transform you from death into life. I challenge you to try it. We, who have accepted Him, know!

CHAPTER VIII

DUST MOTES AND LIGHTNING FLASHES

In the preceding talks, your attention has been directed to a few of the wonders of water. We have seen that this remarkable fluid is necessary for all kinds of life, that the quantity available for the earth must be accurately gauged—neither too much nor too little. The ocean basins must be sufficiently large to hold the water to be lifted from the earth's surface against the force of gravity into the upper atmosphere, so as to provide the 16,000,000 tons of moisture falling every second across the earth.

We have examined some of the surprising ways by which the problems have been solved. We know that the process of evaporation changes the molecules of water into molecules of water-vapor which occupy 1,600 times the space they did as water. This noiseless operation, working continuously throughout the world, would seem to be the product of Omniscience. This aqueous vapor in the form of clouds must now be changed back into water and evenly distributed to the earth—another tremendous problem.

The second clause of Psalm 135:7 tells us that "He makes lightnings (electrical discharges) for the rain." This means that God devised electricity in order to cause the infinitely small molecules of vapor to unite in the form of raindrops, so that they could be precipitated by gravity to the earth. There may be no visible lightning flash, but there is always electricity when there is rain. Another requisite for rain is a dust mote on which the drop can form.

In Proverbs 8:26, there is a mysterious statement about "the highest part of the dust of the world." This dust seems to have been one of the first created things —a necessity for rainfall. It is clear that there must be some means of replenishing this supply which is constantly needed. How can cosmic dust be supplied? Astronomers inform us that at least 20,000,000 meteors visible to the naked eye, broken off from distant worlds, reach our atmosphere every 24 hours and are burned up into dust. In addition to these visible meteoric masses, there are other countless millions which cannot be seen. What an ingenious and satisfactory device! Could any one but God be responsible for this?

How are the immense masses of watery vapor to be moved, so that the water will not fall back into the seas from which they rose? So, the third clause in this remarkable 7th verse of Psalm 135 reads: "He bringeth the wind out of His treasuries."

We have thought of winds as "fickle" but as a matter of fact, they obey definite scientific laws. "The wind returneth again according to its circuits," says Ecclesiastes. Apparently what happens is that the Creator says to the winds, His servants summoned from His treasure house: "Winds, hitch yourselves to these cloud chariots and carry them across the world." The winds obey this command of their Maker, and with great power move rapidly through space, carrying their immense load of water which is dropped on hill and dale, bringing life everywhere.

Ecclesiastes tells us also that the rivers return to their high sources and that is exactly what happens. When the clouds reach the mountain tops, condensation takes place, the clouds empty themselves and the rivers are back once more where they began. Thus—"Unto the place whence the rivers came, thither they return again."

The entire series of operations is conducted with amazing accuracy and ease. Think of the admirable way God has arranged that rain, for the most part, falls in soft and gentle showers. If the clouds poured out their prodigious contents in great streams and floods, the consequences would be tragically destructive. Without this provision for gentle precipitation, vegetation would be destroyed, crops beaten into the ground, trees stripped of leaves and fruit, fields ploughed into deep trenches, and soil washed away. Every passing cloud would be an object of terror. But how beneficient is the existing arrangement! Instead of ruinous cascades of water, it trickles down in gentle and fertilizing drops, as if the clouds were perforated like a sieve. Seldom is a blade of grass hurt or the most delicate flower injured.

Snow and hail, like the rain, descend from the laboratory of the skies. A snowflake is one of God's most beautiful architectural marvels. It is composed of fine, shining spiculae diverging from the center. Falling through the atmosphere, these myriads unite in a mass of flakes. They are infinite in variety and beauty, varying in size from one-thirtieth to one-third of an inch in diameter, Countless billions of these downy flakes are showered upon the earth, every one perfectly formed after its proper model. Each frozen particle of water finds its precise place and position, the great majority being six-sided crystals, each geometrically perfect and differing in figure and symmetry.

Can the human imagination conjure any one but God who possesses wisdom and skill able to create instantly these countless designs of infinite beauty—no two of them alike?

Forethought is seen also in the fact that snow provides a warm blanket for the earth wherever winters are severe. An extreme degree of cold means the death of living things unless a heating device is made available, and so the refreshing rain of summer is changed into snow that descends like soft wool to cover and protect the earth in winter. Settling into a compact layer, the internal heat of the ground is prevented from escaping, so that when spring comes again, life abundant and vigorous emerges from beneath the snow masses.

The mountains of snow piled high on all the ranges serve as an inexhaustible reservoir of water during the heat of summer as this life-giving liquid flows steadily to the panting plains below.

It is said that rain and snow wash down nitrogen in the form of nitrites and nitrates worth several dollars an acre each year, giving strength and vigor to all growing things. Psalm 145:16 is seen to be more than picturesque speech:

"Thou openest Thine hand, and satisfiest the desire of every living thing."

From the very earliest times, the goodness of God in nature has attracted the attention of men and women in every part of the world. An old writing of Hypolytus, one of the early Christian Fathers, born about 150 A.D., and living to be 85 years of age, mentions the subject we are discussing. He says in one of his discourses:

"Good—yea—very good are all the works of our God and Saviour, all of them that eye seeth and mind perceiveth, (all that reason interprets and hand handles, all that intellect comprehends and human nature understands . . .) And what more requisite gift is there than water? For with water all things are washed and nourished and cleaned. Water enriches the earth, produces the dew, exhilarates the vine, matures corn in the ear, ripens the grape cluster, softens the olive, sweetens the palmdate, reddens the rose, decks the violet, and makes the lily to bloom with its brilliant hues.

"Without water the present order of things could not exist. But this is not the only thing that proves the dignity of water.

"There is that which is more honorable than all—the fact that Christ, the Maker of all, came down as the rain (Hosea 6:3), and was known as a 'spring,' diffusing Himself as a river, and being baptized in the Jordan. Here are things strange beyond compare,—how should the boundless River that makes glad the city of God have dipped itself in a little stream? The illimitable Spring that bears life to all men, and has no end, was covered by poor and temporary waters.

"He who is present everywhere, and absent nowhere, He who is incomprehensible to angels, and invisible to men, comes to this baptism according to His own good pleasure, thus revealing His infinite condescension to man. He came to save us from our sins and for this we adore Him—the Water of life." Thus spoke Hypolytus.

Listen to the old prophet Isaiah in chapter 55:
"Ho—every one that thirsteth—come ye to
the waters, and he that hath no money;
come ye, buy and eat; yea, come buy wine
and milk, without money and without
price."

What person of right mind would refuse this gift
from the hand of Omnipotence? Such a rejection would
seem incredible, but the greatest tragedy of this age is
the fact that God is largely ignored—Christ and His
sacrifice for us rejected and even ridiculed while Death
waits to impose the sure penalty of our sin, unless we
accept the One who has borne the penalty.

May I ask you, my friend, is it well with your soul
today? It will pay you to give this matter of supreme
importance your immediate attention. Do not **forget**
that promise of Jesus Christ:

"Whosoever drinketh of the water that I
shall give him shall **never thirst.**"

CHAPTER IX

RIVERS

Today we think of the magnificent system of rivers which furrow the earth, constituting a grand system of drainage and irrigation. The benefits derived from the magnificent network of rivers which cover the globe are obviously incalculable. Besides draining the earth of its surplus waters without which some of the fairest portions of its surface would soon be submerged, they are the means by which living creatures on the dry land are furnished with their needed drink, and man is given a most valuable food supply from the fish bred in the waters.

They also open great channels of commerce with distant and interior countries; while, in their course to the sea, they provide unlimited power and facilities for manufacture. Rivers have built and have furnished the wealth of the most renowned cities of earth, where the richest monuments of art and industry have been assembled.

In Europe we find four great rivers. The Rhone, 400 miles long, drains about 7,000 square miles; the Rhine, 700 miles in length carries to the sea the waters from about 15,000 square miles; the Danube pursues its course for 1,800 miles, taking the waters from an expanse of not less than 55,000 square miles; while the 2,000 mile-long Volga, winding slowly along its course, gathers the waters of one-half of the great Russian Empire.

Asia has a still more magnificent system. China

has two rivers, each more than 3,000 miles long, and Siberia two others of equal size. In Siam there are the Iriwaddi and Maykaung, while in western Asia are the Euphrates and Tigris of ancient memory.

British India has large rivers running for thousands of miles, the most celebrated being the Ganges which leaps into sight for the first time from a perpendicular wall of ice in the Himalayas, and pursuing a course of almost 1,900 miles, draws its "sacred" waters from a district of unequalled fertility, embracing an area of not less than 400,000 square miles.

Africa has comparatively few rivers, the Niger stretching its crooked length for 2,000 miles, and the Nile 3,200 miles long, for the last 800 miles receiving not a single tributary.

In America we find rivers of supreme magnitude and grandeur. The St. Lawrence drains 300,000 square miles; the Mississippi, 4,000 miles long, draws its waters from a surface of 1,000,000 square miles. The Amazon is king of them all and near its mouth presents a stream 100 miles wide and 600 feet deep.

There are ocean rivers which flow as definitely and regularly as the Danube or the Nile. Their channels are established for thousands of miles, as they pursue their course along beds and between banks of other and different water, as fixed as if built of granite rock.

The most remarkable of these is the famous Gulf Stream, so named because it was long supposed to originate in the Gulf of Mexico. Its exact origin is not yet fully known, but Humboldt and others believe that it receives its first impulse near the southern extremity of Africa.

From the Gulf of Mexico this stream flows into the Atlantic between Florida and Cuba, whence it runs northward nearly parallel to the coast of the United States, until it reaches Nova Scotia and Newfoundland, where it makes a great bend, throwing one branch downward toward the Azores, while the other spreads out and flows north to the British Isles, and thence to the Polar Sea.

The banks and bottom of this magnificent river are of cold water while its main stream is warm. It is 70 miles wide, 3,000 feet deep and equal in volume to more than a thousand Mississippis at full flood. Along the Florida coast its speed is about 80 miles a day, but by the time it has reached the Azores, it has slowed down to ten miles a day. Its color, as far as the coasts of the Carolinas, is indigo blue. Its banks or edges are well defined with the middle of the stream considerably higher than the edges, so that it runs like a serpentine ridge upon the surface of the ocean. What is still more remarkable, it runs up hill. In part of its course the gradient of its bed is not less than five or six feet to the mile.

Its most notable characteristic is its effect on climate due to its high temperature. As it leaves the Gulf of Mexico its temperature is 86 degrees F. After traversing ten degrees of latitude, it remains at 84 degrees, and when it has travelled 3,000 miles north, it still preserves in winter the heat of summer. Continuing its course, it overflows its liquid banks and spreads over thousands of square miles a mantle of warmth. This heat is carried by the west winds over all the west coast of Europe, softening and ameliorating its climate.

Thus the British Isles are made habitable, even though in the same latitude as Labrador, which is bound in the grip of ice and snow. Life is made possible in Norway and Sweden, where otherwise eternal cold would prevail.

In view of these considerations, are we not justified in believing that the Gulf Stream is another evidence of our God's design and forethought?

Scarcely less remarkable is the Japanese Current, which runs along the Pacific Coast and has a somewhat similar effect there. Then there is the great Polar Stream bearing down in the opposite direction to the Gulf Stream—a sort of compensatory current. This rises in the distant recesses of Baffin's Bay and the Greenland Sea and, studded with icebergs, sweeps along the coast of Labrador, encircling the island of Newfoundland in its chill embrace. As it journeys south, it encounters the Gulf Stream running north-westward. As the paths of these two giants cross each other, they seem to struggle for right of way. Their hostile waters refuse to mingle and each continues to retain its color and temperature. From the force of the shock, the Gulf Stream falters in its course, momentarily, and is deflected towards the South. The Polar current, unable to break through the mass of water in the Gulf Stream, dives under its bed and hastens on to the tropics, bringing its refreshing coolness to these heatridden countries.

It is obvious that by reason of this perpetual circulation of the waters of the deep—the streams flowing from and to the equator—not only is the rigorous cold of the polar regions relieved, but the exhausting heat of the tropics is modified.

There is another interesting fact. The streams which flow from the Polar Seas toward the South carry along with them vast numbers of excellent fish from the colder latitudes. In this way there is supplied to the people of the warmer regions, food which could not be found in the heated waters of the southern seas.

As we view our globe in its outlines of land and water, with its manifold and complicated arrangements, we are able to see a bit of God's mind as He formed and fashioned, measured and weighed, and imposed His divine will on all the details of this marvelous system. When the waters gathered themselves, it was not at random but in strict conformity to His plan. When the various currents devised by Him began to circulate, there was no chance but rather Omniscience in action. No wonder God pronounced everything "good."

Rivers add greatly to the beauty of our world. Our God has provided us with innumerable objects which charm the eye and ravish our senses.

Some day Christ will once more visit the earth and will reign in person as King of kings and Lord of lords. We read in Isaiah, the 33d chapter, verses 20 and 21, of "Jerusalem, a quiet habitation, a place of broad rivers and streams wherein shall go no galley with oars, neither shall gallant ship pass thereby." What a charming picture of restful beauty! How we covet that quietness which is almost impossible to secure today because of the increasing demands of business and the thouand and one things which distract our minds and unsettle our spirits. Most of us long for an afternoon by the riverside sitting under the shade of widespreading branches, just to read and meditate without the marring intrusions of clanging telephone bells or the raucous noises which characterize our every day life. When God once again assumes control and takes over the helm of this sinking ship, which we call "our world," then we shall indeed "rest in the Lord."

This will be the reward conferred upon all those who have taken that living water which only Christ can supply. It is offered freely to every individual, but before it can effect its remarkable transformation, there must be a definite and personal act of acceptance from the Lord who offers it. It can work no miracles, if it is refused. In other words, what is required is a decision—an act of the will which involves not only a sense of sin and a knowledge of the penalty of sin, but a change of attitude toward Jesus Christ. Sufficient living water is available for the salvation of all people on earth. This does not by any means guarantee that all will be saved, as some seem to think. It does guarantee eternal life to all who make the great decision.

It is a tragic and undoubted fact that comparatively few are willing to accept this freely-offered gift of God, and here is a mystery. Is it possible to explain why intelligent men and women, hearing this "good news" of God's amazing offer which brings absolute pardon for sin and an eternity in heaven, without price, will turn a deaf ear preferring eternal death, which is the only alternative?

Once more I ask you to listen to what God, Himself, has to say, as recorded in Isaiah, the 55th chapter:
> "Ho, every one that thirsteth, come ye to the waters, and he that hath no money; come ye, buy and eat; yea, come, buy wine and milk without money and without price. Wherefore do ye spend money for that which is not bread? and your earnings for that which satisfieth not? Hearken diligently unto Me . . . Incline your ear and come unto Me; hear and your soul shall live."

Will you do this today?

CHAPTER X

HUMANS LIVING IN AN OCEAN

Today we direct our thoughts to the atmosphere. We live at the bottom of a vast ocean of air which extends to a height of about 200 miles. Man's exploration of this huge expanse has been confined to extremely narrow limits. He has ascended about nine miles in an airplane and about thirteen miles in a balloon, while the greatest height ever reached by a sounding balloon is only about 24 miles.

The density of our gaseous envelope is greatest near the earth's surface, and gradually becomes thinner as the altitude increases. About half its weight is within four miles of the earth, although minute traces of air are believed to exist even at a height of 2,000 miles.

The weight of the atmosphere is a very important item about which there could be no chance. The air-pressure at sea level is nearly fifteen pounds to every square inch of surface—an average of fourteen tons upon every person. About one ton of air rests upon every square foot of surface. This exact weight is due, obviously to two factors, the weight of the gases composing the atmosphere and the height to which the air goes. A slight change in either of these conditions might result in a greatly increased pressure or, on the other hand, greatly reduced. The former would crush by its weight and the latter would bring about death, possibly through hemorrhage and also inability to breathe the rarified air, as on top of the highest mountains.

Of course, in addition to these two factors, is the presence of watery vapor, another condition on which life depends, and behind all these must be placed the size and weight of the earth determining the atmospheric mantle.

If the weight and size of the earth were doubled, every object would have its weight doubled. The atmosphere would press down with two fold force; respiration would be labored and painful. Water would weigh twice as much and sap could not ascend. Tools and implements would be so heavy that they would be unwieldly, every mechanical operation in field and workshop would require twice as much energy. Every animal would move as though loaded down with another of equal size or weight. Men could barely crawl about with strength exhausted in bearing their own weight, Winds would tear down all houses, if they had not already fallen by their own weight. Rain, hail and floods would exert a tremendously destructive force.

If the earth were only half its size and weight, equally death-dealing would be the results, with air too light to sustain life. Sap would ascend too rapidly. Men and animals would move about very unsteadily and slowly without sufficient ballast. Life could not go on.

These facts cause us to pay attention to the statement in Job 28:24, 25: "For He looketh to the end of the earth, and seeth under the whole heaven; To make the weight for the winds; He weigheth the waters by measure."

How may we account for this remarkable scientific item written down so long ago unless we believe in a supernatural God and in a supernatural Book?

With the exception of water vapor, the percentage

of which may vary between wide limits, the constituents of the air are relatively constant in amount. The average composition of dry air is as follows by volume: Nitrogen, 78 per cent; Oxygen, 21 per cent; Carbon Dioxide, .04 per cent; Argon, .96 per cent, with slight traces of Neon, Helium, Krypton, Xenon, Hydrogen and Ozone. In addition, of course, the air contains dust particles, bacteria, and minute quantities of certain gases caused by manufacturing processes—compounds of Sulphur with Oxygen and Hydrogen. The constituents of air are not chemically united. They are merely mixed— a device which shows again the wisdom of the Creator.

Think of the gases which make up 99 per cent of the air—Nitrogen, 78 per cent, and Oxygen 21 per cent. Nitrogen serves to dilute the Oxygen, thus retarding burning and oxidation, and is necessary as a plant food. Oxygen is necessary for respiration, to support combustion, and to aid decay of organic matter. The delicate balance of these two gases, the constancy of their proportions in the atmosphere, the admirable way in which they operate for their designed purpose, must be because there was thought and planning somewhere.

Of the 92 elements known to man, not one is more important than Oxygen. Man breathes it every moment of the day and night, and so is enabled to carry on his life processes. He uses it to help burn the fuels that cook his foods, that warm his home and generate power to operate his machinery. He depends on oxygen to decay waste materials, destroy germs, and purify water. In hospitals, submarines, mines and airplanes, it is put to vitally important uses.

Nitrogen is by far the most abundant substance in the air. It is an inert or "lazy" gas, not combining readily with other substances. The fact that it is abundant and inert is seen to be very necessary. If the air were composed entirely or largely of Oxygen, all burning would take place with extreme vigor, and it would be practically impossible to control a fire, once started. Nitrogen therefore, dilutes the Oxygen to the point where it is just active enough for our needs. How was this proportion arranged? Certainly not by chance!

Nitrogen is an important constituent of all plants and animals, but most living things are unable to extract it from the vast atmosphere reservoir about them. They depend on certain tiny plants, belonging to the bacteria class, which have the ability to extract Nitrogen from the air. In this way, Nitrogen is made available for all other living things. And man has now succeeded in tapping the great stores of Nitrogen in the air by using powerful electric currents, a process known as fixation of Nitrogen.

In all these studies we have observed that there is plan and forethought and in regard to the atmosphere, this is clearly apparent. In the passage from Job previously mentioned, we are told that "God understandeth . . . for He looketh to the end of the earth . . . (in order) to make a weight for the wind."

What a startling and suggestive expression! The only possible meaning is that this important item was considered and arranged by the Creator. In order that there might be suitable life conditions, He has given us thousands of instances of His planning. If we apply our reason to this subject, there is one inevitable conclusion and that is, that there is a personal God exerting His supreme wisdom and power at every point.

Besides these wonderful properties and functions of the atmosphere, it is the appointed medium of many

other inestimable benefits to the world in which we
live.

While the sun is the great source of light, yet the
co-operation of the atmosphere to diffuse the light is
essential to the proper illumination of the earth. To
the atmosphere we must ascribe the glories of the day,
the lovely blue of the heavens and the soft and sooth-
ing shades of the landscape.

Without it, the sky would be black as ebony, and
out of it the sun would gleam like a red-hot ball; and
his beams, like a ray passing through an aperture into
a dark room, would reveal only the objects on which
they fell, or those from which they were directly re-
flected. Without atmosphere, there would be no twilight, no morning, no evening. The sun at the dawn of
day would burst from the bosom of night in all its un-
bearable brilliance; and at the close of day, would suddenly plunge out of view, leaving us suddenly in utter
darkness. To the atmosphere we owe all the glories of
the setting sun, when the heavens put on their most
glorious robes to thrill us with celestial beauty.

By means of atmosphere birds wing their way
through space, and insects flit from flower to flower.
Without it the eagle and condor would flap their wings
in vain and flight would be impossible. The atmosphere
is also the medium for sound and smell. Without it,
eternal silence would reign, and music would be impossible. Conversation and song would be unknown.

This vast and wonderful appendage of our globe
has been made to meet the nature and wants of the
living creatures and growing vegetation that occupy its
surface. Design and mutual adaptation are very manifest. We have exactly those elements in just the proportions essential to the life and health of all creatures.

The atmosphere has been made for the lungs; and lungs have been made for atmosphere. How beautiful the adjustment whereby animals breathe oxygen and liberate carbon dioxide, plants using the carbon and setting oxygen free for the use of animals!

The atmosphere and the ear have been formed one for the other. In like manner the atmosphere and organs of speech have been formed in mutual adaptation. You are hearing my voice because of these planned features. And the message I would like you to get from this brief talk is that which would bring you into vital contact with the One who has made all this possible.

How can we ignore these manifestations of Omniscience and Omnipotence? God has spoken. Shall we listen? What about a few moments of quiet thought regarding your relation to the Lord Jesus Christ? I can assure you He will give you pardon and joy and peace, if you will accept Him as Saviour.

It may be that now the world with all its distractions looms large on your horizon. You are fretted and worried by the countless "things" which fill each day, and yet you do not seem to be getting anywhere. You may be a worldly Christian getting little joy out of your Christian life. Give Christ a chance!

"Hast thou heard Him, seen Him, known Him?
Is not thine a raptured heart?
Chief among ten thousand, own Him,
Gladly choose the better part.

What has stripped the seeming beauty
From the idols of the earth?
Not the sense of right or duty,
But the sight of peerless worth.

Not the crushing of the idols,
With its bitter void and smart,
But the beaming of His beauty,
The unveiling of His heart.

'Tis that look that melted Peter,
'Tis that face that Stephen saw,
'Tis that heart that wept with Mary,
Can alone from idols draw.

Draw and win and fill completely,
Till the cup o'erflow the brim.
What have we to do with idols
Who have companied with HIM?"

CHAPTER XI

GOD'S VENTILATING SYSTEM

We have seen that nitrogen is made available by small plants. Plants and animals need this gas in order to build protein, an essential substance present in the tissues and organs of all living things. Corn, wheat, oats and all other common crops remove great quantities of this element from the soil. This may be replaced, of course, by artificial fertilizers containing nitrogen in the form of certain chemical compounds with potassium, sodium, and ammonia.

The method by which the nitrogen in the air may be seized upon and appropriated by nature is exceedingly interesting. Certain common leguminous plants, such as beans, peas, clover and alfalfa have attached to their roots certain round structures known as nodules which contain types of bacteria able to convert the inert nitrogen of the air into useful nitrogen compounds. Some of these are absorbed by the plants and the remainder are left in the soil to enrich it. Who would ever imagine that these microscopic organisms could be so useful? Was it accident which placed them in the ground?

The action of lightning is another means of fixing atmospheric nitrogen. During a thunderstorm, small amounts of nitrogen and oxygen are caused to combine, forming compounds that are dissolved by rain water and carried down to the ground.

The feature which arrests our attention is the ingenious way in which this necessary element is made available for plants, and then for animals and humans. Without it life would not be possible, but while free in vast quantities, it must be captured in a very special manner. The plan we have so briefly discussed is admirable in every way.

The gas, Carbon Dioxide, which is the product of combustion in animals and man, must be disposed of. Otherwise, as it is breathed out in great quantities and released in other ways, life would become impossible. But here is where the divine plan comes in. The plants are eagerly waiting for every bit of Carbon Dioxide we can give them, and drink it in eagerly through their wide-open mouths present in countless thousands on their leaves.

The presence of water-vapor in the air is another evidence of design. As we have seen, this vapor is constantly arising from oceans, lakes, rivers, and other bodies of water. When the amount of water-vapor in the air becomes excessive, it is changed into rain, snow, hail, fog, dew, or frost, depending on the existing conditions.

The humidity of the air is of great importance to the health of all living things. Without water-vapor in the atmosphere over the earth, a condition would exist similar to that on the moon. The surface of the moon is very hot, as the sun shines on it, but immediately after the sun's rays disappear, heat is succeeded by the most intense cold—almost 200 degrees below zero. The reason for this is the absence of water-vapor which holds in its folds the heat received during the day, gradually releasing it through the hours of the night, but so slowly that man is not caused any suffering. Another blanket may have to be pulled over the bed about 4:00 a.m., but that is all. If the night were much longer, it is easy to see how death would result. The moisture in the air then keeps us warm—God's blanket over His children.

We cannot close this study without a brief mention of winds. Without winds the air would be calm and dead. Noxious and irritating vapors, and objectionable odors would distress and disturb humanity daily, but God's thought went ahead and provided a solution. A wind, of course, is a movement of air along the earth's surface. Differences of temperature and air pressure are the two basic factors which produce such movements of air, ranging in intensity from the gentle summer breeze to the dreaded West Indian hurricane.

When air is heated, it expands and becomes lighter than that of an adjacent region. Immediately the colder, heavier air flows along the earth's surface to the warmer region, and pushes the lighter air upwards. This air is then carried across the upper atmosphere where it is cooled. It then descends, thus completing its cycle. It is the horizontal movement of air we call wind.

And so difference of pressure and temperature on sea and land causes the delightful and invigorating land and sea breezes. During the day the earth absorbs heat more rapidly than the water. This causes the air over the land to become warmer and lighter than the air over the water, so a cool breeze from the water area flows in toward the land during the afternoon— a sea breeze.

At night the land loses heat more rapidly than the water, thus causing the air over the water to become warmer, and lighter than the air over the land. Consequently there is a flow of colder, heavier air during the night and early morning hours from the land to the water—the land breeze. What a beneficent arrangement by a loving Creator!

The great differences in temperature and air pressure between the equatorial and polar regions give rise to large scale movements of air. These movements are modified by the rotation of the earth, thus establishing a system of alternating wind belts and belts of calm over the earth's surface.

Of these various belts, the trade winds are perhaps the most interesting and certainly they are very beneficial as a means of transportation. There are regions on either side of the equator in which the air is moving steadily from both sides toward the equator. The rotation of the earth causes a deflection of the winds, so that they flow from the northeast in the northern hemisphere, and from the southeast in the southern hemisphere. Ships navigating these areas can always count on the presence of these trade winds.

When we think of these interesting features of our globe, we are accustomed to having them described as among the wonders of Nature, but we must always remember that God is not Nature and Nature is not God.

Whatever of wisdom or wonder, of goodness or excellence, Nature displays, existed in the divine Mind from eternity. The end of every created thing is to be a manifestation of the Creator's perfections.

We have been thinking of lightning. This tremendous display of celestial electricity strikes our vision and excites either fear or amazement, but no one understands it. God uses it in His own mysterious way. Who has not shuddered in the midst of a violent electrical storm, as these blinding flashes of light cut across the sky accompanied by deafening peals of thunder, as if God were striking the anvils of heaven with His mighty hammer?

When the storm has spent its force, what a happy transfiguration of all Nature! The sultry and oppressive atmosphere has disappeared. The sun shines forth with softened splendor while the foliage glistens with lingering raindrops and a refreshed landscape seems to rejoice because the world has been blessed and renovated by the storm.

So it is with the storms of life. It may be that your moral atmosphere needs clearing, and your soul requires new health. Our storms may startle and dismay, but they are sent in mercy to bring us, it may be, into a consciousness of our need of a higher Power.

Someone has put it this way:

"Ofttimes the heavy tempests round me blow,
And o'er my soul the waves and billows go,
But when the storms beat loudest, and I cry
Aloud for help, the Master standeth by,
And whispers to my soul, 'Lo, it is I.'
Above the tempest wild I hear Him say,
'Beyond the darkness lies the perfect day;
In every path of thine, I lead the way.'"

Even now, someone listening to me may be in fear of a tempest rising on your horizon. There is a sure Refuge for you, if you will have it. You are restless, and weary, and burdened. Will you hear the voice of Him Who is able to carry out every promise He has ever made? And here is a glorious word from Him: "Come unto me, all ye that labour and are heavy laden, and I will give you rest."

Most of us long for a period of relief from the noise and turmoil and worry of this twentieth century. There is one and only one sure haven where the wildest storm can never bring the slightest ripple to the surface of the still waters. That haven is the Lord Jesus Christ.

May I say that I have found in Him not only a Saviour but all the other blessings that He confers on His children. Is it worth while to pass up this magnificent opportunity for eternal life and eternal glory for the future, and indescribable blessings for the present? What about your getting in touch with Him today?

> "For God so loved the world that He gave His only begotten Son that whosoever believeth in Him should not perish but have everlasting life."

CHAPTER XII

NATURE'S BUILDING BLOCKS

Now I ask your attention to some thoughts on Matter — that lifeless, mysterious stuff of which the universe, including our earth, is made.

There are 92 elements, which constitute all kinds of matter, from hydrogen at one end of the scale to uranium at the other. Matter is formed from particles known as molecules which are a combination of atoms. Inside the atoms science affirms there are infinitely minute particles called electrons, thought to be charges of negative electricity. Each atom also is said to contain one proton which is a charge of positive electricity. Other curious and infinitely small particles, such as neutrons and positrons have also been discovered in the atom, as science seeks to unravel the unfathomable mystery of Matter.

Hydrogen, the first element in the table, is the extremely light, inflammable gas which the Germans used to fill their Zeppelins. It is one of the constituent parts of water and is found in many other substances. Its presence in fuels is usually revealed by the blue flame produced.

The atom of hydrogen has, as far as science has been able to determine, only one positively charged particle, or proton, in its nucleus. Around this, is the swiftly moving, negatively charged electron.

Though the two particles exactly counter-balance each other in electrical charge, the mass of the proton has been calculated as being 1845 times as great as the mass of the electron. Thus the proton accounts for practically the entire mass of the atom.

The nucleus of the atom may contain more than one proton. As we proceed upward from hydrogen in the table of elements, we find more and more protons and even electrons squeezed into the relatively small nucleus. When we reach uranium, the complexity of the atoms of the elements has greatly increased. In the atomic nucleus of uranium, there are said to be 92 protons and 146 neutrons along with 92 out-revolving electrons.

In addition to the 92 elements, there are many compounds—substances whose building blocks consist of combinations of atoms of various elements. Theodore L. Handrich writes interestingly in his book, "Every-Day Science," about them and every student gazes with astonishment at what he sees on examination of these mysterious substances.

The water molecule consists of two hydrogen atoms and one oxygen atom. These molecules, which are fundamental units of matter, vary from the simplest, as those of water, to others containing thousands of atoms all combined in definite proportions and patterns. A crystalline protein molecule from the juice of diseased tobacco plants apparently consists of about 2,000,000 atoms. A slight change in the proportion of one element to another in a molecule can alter the compound so radically that it has entirely different properties.

Between hydrogen and uranium lie all the other elements with many differing combinations, each obeying some rigid law which governs its operations. There must be an infinite Mind behind the origin of Matter to bring into being these infinitesimal particles, and then cause them to combine in innumerable ways according to some prearranged plan. Will any such terms as Struggle for Existence or Survival of the Fittest suffice as an explanation of their existence? Could these lifeless particles possibly create themselves? The question answers itself.

While the 92 kinds of atoms are distinct and separate, those of each particular form are absolutely similar in structure and performance. As Graebner says: "They are like coins struck in a mint, each bearing the impress of the image of their Maker in the attributes they possess."

Another wonderful feature of atoms is that, while those of the same element are alike in size, shape, weight, and other properties, the electrons in all the elements are identical as to their properties. This suggests the ultimate identity of all the elements in the constitution of all Matter. Different kinds of Matter, therefore, would differ only in having different numbers of electrons with different velocities within or around their fields of positive electrification or around their positive nuclei.

And if the proton portion of the atom consists of granular particles, then these particles, like the electrons, must be also the same for all the so-called chemical elements. In other words, all Matter would be composed of the same electrons, protons, deuterons, positrons, neutrons, differing only in their numbers, arrangements and revolutions.

Is the human mind able to contemplate anything more amazing than this? Such a conception and the power to make it work belong only to Deity.

The chemical laws which compel these elements to combine according to atomic weights, and the law of multiple proportions, show the infinite wisdom of the Creator. Each atom of Matter is stamped with laws that are definite and invariable so that it acts with absolute precision in all that it does. Thirty-two pounds of sulphur must have 50 pounds of iron with which to unite, no more, no less, and so with all the elements.

In these various chemical compounds are found molecules of varying complexity with atoms of increasing number. From water with its three atoms, nitric acid with five, caffeine with 24, quinine with 48, we pass on up to the mysterious protein molecule with hundreds and thousands of atoms, a formation which staggers the imagination.

L. J. Henderson writes in "The Order of Nature," p. 201:

> "The properties of elements are to be regarded as fully determined from the earliest conceivable epoch, and perfectly changeless in time."

L. Franklin Gruber, writing in "Whence Came the Universe," remarks:

> "What skill or intelligence must be necessary to build up such complex infinitesimal structures in their countless duplicates, all exactly alike for the same substance. Yet so wonderful are the workings of nature's mysterious laboratory that no two of the same kind among the countless number of these molecules, wherever found throughout nature, differ in the least detail. Surely a law is operative here that requires an infinitely intelligent Law-Giver."

It is not difficult to picture a mighty Creator when we view great mountain ranges stretching across the earth for thousands of miles, but this God of Nature exhibits His skill and wisdom and power more in the infinitesimal than in the things which we can see. Even a slight acquaintance with these infinitely small particles of Matter to which we have been directing our thought, enables us to appreciate the exultant cry of Deut. 3:24. Listen:

> "O Lord God, thou hast begun to show thy servant thy greatness, and thy mighty hand: for what God is there in heaven, or in earth, that can do according to thy works, and according to thy might?"

The question asked by Asaph in Psalm 77, verse 13, echoes down through the ages to us today and finds an instant response in our hearts: "Who is so great a God as our God?"

It will not be amiss to hear what the Bible has to say about this God of ours. In Deut. 4:39, I read:

> "Know therefore this day, and consider it in thine heart, that the Lord is God in heaven above, and upon the earth beneath: there is none else."

Thousands of years ago, Eliphaz seems to have been wiser than many of us today, when he wrote in the 5th chapter of Job, verse 8:

> "I would seek unto God and unto God would I commit my cause; who doeth great things and unsearchable; marvelous things without number; who giveth rain upon the earth and sendeth waters upon the fields: to set up on high those that be low."

I believe, if all this be true, and I am very sure it is true, then we can agree with him when he brings the comforting assurance of verses 18 to 27:

> "For he maketh sore and bindeth up; he woundeth and his hands make whole. He will deliver thee in six troubles; yea, in seven there shall no evil touch thee. In famine He shall redeem thee from death; and in war from the power of the sword. Thou shalt be hid from the scourge of the tongue; neither shalt thou be afraid of destruction when it cometh. At destruction and death, thou shalt laugh. Neither shalt thou be afraid of the beasts of the earth. For thou shalt be in league with the stones of the field: and the beasts of the field shall be at peace with thee. And thou shalt know that thy tent is in peace. And thou shalt visit thy fold, and shalt miss nothing . . . Lo this, we have searched it, so it is: hear it and know thou it for thy good."

This series of benefits accruing to those who take God as their Friend are certainly worth while. As for me, I am going to take advantage of this fellowship. I have made this God, who can do all these things, my God. I know this Book speaks exact truth.

I challenge you, who are listening to me, if you have not already done so, to prove Phil. 4:19:

> "My God shall supply **all** your need according to his riches in glory by Christ Jesus."

If you will link up with this wonderful "Man of Galilee," He will save you for time and eternity. Can you afford to neglect this great chance? Do it **now.**

CHAPTER XIII

THE MOST MYSTERIOUS SUBSTANCE IN THE UNIVERSE

The wonders of Protoplasm, the basic material of all living bodies, is a subject well worth our careful study. It is the most mysterious substance in the universe. Biologists have tried ceaselessly to produce living Protoplasm from non-living substances. All attempts have signally failed, as we would expect them to fail, knowing something of the wonders of this amazing material.

The following elements enter into the composition of all living bodies: carbon, hydrogen, oxygen, nitrogen, sulphur, phosphorus, chlorine, potassium, sodium, calcium, magnesium, iron, with small amounts of fluorine and iodine in some—fourteen in all.

A living cell is made up of many atoms of carbon, hydrogen, oxygen, and nitrogen, with a small number of atoms of sulphur and phosphorus. The diameter of the living molecule is about one five-millionth of an inch, so that a speck of Protoplasm one ten-thousandth of an inch in diameter would require not less than 500 of such molecules in a row to span it, and there would be no less than 125,000,000 of such molecules in the mass. To hope to create a bacillus would be as absurd as to expect to be able to manufacture a human body.

A brief glance at the wonders of Protoplasm will show the absurdity of holding the view that once upon a time a fortuitous concourse of atoms was the accidental cause of this greatest of all mysteries.

Living matter shows four distinct phenomena:

1. Irritability—the property of responding in a particular way to the application of a stimulus.

2. Metabolism—the chemical changes produced as food materials are built up into higher forms and complex molecules already built up are broken down and their effete products are excreted.

3. Growth—increase in the size of the particular body until it reaches its destined form.

4. Reproduction—the process by which each living body insures the continuation of itself through its descendants.

These four processes constitute the operation of these microscopic bits of Protoplasm called cells from which various other tissues are ultimately formed by a series of complex and exact changes which are impossible to understand, so great is their intricacy. Each bit of living tissue seems to take its place in the line-up as if under the strictest orders from General Headquarters—G. H. Q.

The internal structure of these protoplasmic units reveals a thickened central portion known as the nucleus, surrounded by food material known as cytoplasm. In this latter, there may be pigment granules, fat globules, glycogen particles, and spaces containing fluid. The most important part of the cell consists of chromatin threads which are to form into the miraculous chromosomes, the basis of all the changing forms of life, and all this in a tiny particle of tissue only about one one-hundred-and-twenty-fifth of an inch in diameter. If you would like to know how large that is, sharpen a lead pencil to a fine point, press it gently on a piece of paper, and there you are. That is our size, by the way, as we begin to develop. The manner in which these cells divide and re-divide into countless thousands and millions, separating themselves into various groups to form the different tissues and organs, is an astounding miracle of miracles.

We have mentioned chromatin threads, the basis of the chromosomes. A brief study of these living forms will bring us face to face with God.

Each of us is a complex being, different from every other person of the past or future. No two blades of grass are exact duplicates; neither are any two minds or bodies. Nature varies inheritance with a mathematical precision which prevents the exact duplication of any organ. Nearly all living things begin with the fusing of two sex-cells, one from the male and the other from the female. This is fertilization, whereupon development begins. The single fertilized cell thus formed divides into two cells, these into four, the four into eight, and so on, until in time, there are millions of cells organized into the complete unit, plant or animal, as the case may be.

These processes form a complicated chain, but they go forward with miraculous precision to the predestined end, and in so doing, they give rise to innumerable questions. If all living things are thus formed, why are they not all alike? Why, for example, is John Doe six feet tall, blue-eyed, with straight blond hair, while his brother Jim is a bare five-feet-five, with dark eyes and curly hair? Why do trees have roots and trunks and limbs? Why do fish have fins instead of hands? Why do mules have long ears and practically no power of reproduction? The fascinating answer to all these questions is in one small word—genes.

The scientific definition of a gene is a "minute organic particle, capable of reproduction, located in a chromosome and responsible for the transmission of a hereditary characteristic." This definition contains only statements of fact for which there is suffcient experimental evidence to prove them beyond reasonable doubt.

To understand this definition we must begin with a description of cells. Cells, then, are no more uniform in structure than automobiles. They range in size from those of the bacteria which are on the very limit of microscopic visibility, to nerve cells several feet in length; while in volume they range from an infinitesimal nothing to that of an ostrich egg. Nevertheless, they are all alike in many respects. All living cells are filled with water, and moving through this water is the substance called Protoplasm. As we have noticed, in this Protoplasm is a denser spot known as the nucleus. Until a cell is ready to split in two, the nucleus is a tangle of chromatin threads. As the cells prepare to split, the threads shorten and thicken, forming segments whose number is characteristic of the kind of cell—in man, the number is 48. These rod-like segments are the chromosomes and are made up of strings of genes. If we think of a string of beads, we may get a clearer idea, the entire string standing for the chromosome and the individual beads for the separate genes.

The remarkable facts, which have just been presented, strongly support the great truth which these talks stress—the undoubted evidences of marvelous plan in every detail which we have examined. When we think of these infinitely small particles of material constituting the essential structure of the tiny beads on the string, called genes, our imagination reels at the intricate and accurately working mechanisms which carry on their operations ceaselessly and with absolute precision. These ultra-microscopic bits of chromatin tissue seem to have a definite program laid out for them by an unseen Power—a Power which they must obey under all conditions of environment. They appear on the scene, and immediately begin their destined career without any visible direction; yet they never make a misstep, proceeding from one phase to another until their work is done. Then, they die, are buried, their places taken by new groups that suddenly enter the struggle, and carry on as their predecessors have done from time immemorial.

Let me ask you again: Is it possible to believe there is not a controlling Intelligence behind all this exactitude? These protoplasmic atoms by countless millions have been doing their job with meticulous precision for thousands of years. It would be amazing, if we could show that only one gene or chromosome could exhibit such miraculous powers, but when we know that infinite numbers of them are performing these wonders constantly, our minds are forced to the conclusion there must be a God.

No God of man's making could do these things. Many times the Bible directs us to consider the works of God and then, when we understand what has been done, we are asked to worship. Job tells us that even the animals, if they could speak, would certainly give their testimony in regard to this amazing God. There were many skeptics in Job's time, and he turns on them in the 12th chapter and says:

> "No doubt but ye are the people, and wisdom shall die with you. But I have understanding as well as you; I am not inferior to you: yes, who knoweth not such things as these? I am one mocked of his neighbor

who calleth upon God, and He answereth
him: the just, upright man is laughed to
scorn . . . But ask now the beasts, and they
shall teach thee; and the fowls of the air,
and they shall tell thee: or speak to the
earth, and it shall teach thee; and the fishes of the sea shall declare unto thee. Who
knoweth not in all these that the hand of
the Lord hath wrought this? In whose
hand is the soul of every living thing, and
the breath of all mankind."

As I listen to these strong words from this wise
man of long ago, I am compelled to admit he speaks
truth. Do you not agree?

If you have not considered the inescapable result
of a careless neglect of these issues, let me urge you to
think of your attitude toward the great Creator, who
will call us to account on a day which may not be far
distant. Can you meet Him without fear? You can if
you know that you are His child through faith in Jesus Christ.

CHAPTER XIV

STRINGS OF BEADS

Our subject today is the protoplasmic cell with its miraculous chromosomes and genes—the beads on the string, of which I have already given you some details.

In the last few years, the ultramicroscope and X-rays have given us a much better insight into what these genes are and how they perform their intricate operations. The evidence indicates that they are single complex protein molecules; that they reproduce by "growing" a new gene inside the old one, rather than by splitting in two; that in the chromosome they form strings held together by some unknown force; and that the order of the genes in these strings determines the characteristics of the particular cell containing them. In size they range up to 6 and 7 millionths of a centimeter in diameter.

In higher orders of life, there are thousands of these genes present in each cell, strung out like beads. Changes, called mutations, occur when these strings "cross over" and interchange some of their genes. From these changes result white races or black, geniuses or dolts, men or women. If mutations occurred at random, we might expect extreme changes in an organism from generation to generation, instead of the general similarities which carry through, but mice give birth to mice, and human beings reproduce human beings because of this inherent nature of their respective chromosomes. They work according to an absolutely inviolable law. Where and how did this law originate unless from a Supreme Law-giver?

When chromosomes get together and trade genes, they deal only with those chromosomes which are similar to themselves. For instance and as a crude illustration, let us imagine a community made up of French, Swedes, English, etc., each of whom has several commodities to barter, but French will exchange only with French, Swedes with Swedes, and so on. It will easily be seen that the distribution of wealth in the community will be changed much less under these conditions than if all the residents got together and traded indiscriminately.

Similarly the chromosomes in a nucleus discriminate in favor of their own type, and thus the exchange of genes is not a random thing but is controlled to such an extent that like produces like. It is not hard for a Bible believer to understand this for ten times over in the first chapter of Genesis we read the words, "after its kind." How did Moses know so much about the mysterious laws of genetics in that far-off day unless divinely inspired?

When a cell splits, the chromosomes also split along their length, and each cell then receives its full complement of these priceless genes, presence of which is essential to continuity of life, of organization, of species. But if each cell has its full allotment of genes, one would think that the number must double each generation, when the two-sex cells combine into one. In a remarkable way, this is prevented. When cells which are to become sex-cells split away from their parent-cells, they are automatically endowed with only half the usual number of chromosomes. It is as if some omnipotent Power says to a forming sex-cell: "Wait. When you grow up, you will be a sex-cell. Take only half as many chromosomes. You are going to find a mate with an equal number and everything will be right."

Is it possible for any one familiar with these wonders not to believe in a personal, designing, omnipotent and omniscient God? So we see that life is far more than a mere mechanical process. The body of an organism is much more than a machine. This is just as true of a plant as of an animal. Dr. D. H. Scott, eminent British botanist, wrote in "Extinct Plants and Problems of Evolution," p. 225:

> "The leaves are a mechanism; the stem is a mechanism; and so is the plant as a whole. But the general design and the scheme of the machine were laid down once for all years ago and have never been departed from."

Who, it is pertinent to ask, laid down the plan? The answer again is **God.** This unchanging purpose runs through the entire system of plant life.

No one knows what this life principle is. It cannot be examined, and science is completely in the dark as to its nature. We see how it works, but its real character eludes all efforts to discover it.

As Dr. Alfred Russel Wallace wrote, thirty years ago in "The World of Life," p. 3, so is the mystery today:

> "So marvelous and so varied are the phenomena presented by living things, so completely do their powers transcend those of all other forms of matter subjected to mechanical, physical or chemical laws, that biologists have vainly endeavored to find out what is at the bottom of their

strange manifestations, and to give precise definitions, in terms of physical science, of what 'life' really is."

Horatio Hackett Newman, geologist, wrote in "The Nature and Origin of the World and of Man," p. 52:

"In all frankness it must be admitted that the problem of the origin of life has not been solved."

General Smuts, as quoted by Graebner in "God and the Cosmos," p. 129, said:

"Recent astronomical theory has come to strengthen this view of life as an exceptional feature of the main track of the universe. For the origin of our planetary system is attributed to an unusual accident, and planets such as ours with a favorable chance for life are taken to be rare in the universe. Perhaps we may even say at the present epoch there is no other globe where life is at the level manifested on earth."

He could more properly have said that life is unknown at all anywhere except on this globe.

James S. Haldane, distinguished physiologist, affirmed that:

"The mechanistic speculations of the last century no longer afford any prospect of understanding life."

Professor Conn agrees in the following words:

"There is not the slightest evidence that living matter could arise from non-living matter. Spontaneous generation is universally given up."

And yet men will persist in the unscientific assertion that life came from dead matter sometime, somehow in the long ago.

It is a common diversion among those who hold the Bible in small esteem, to express themselves in opposition to its statements about the origin of man, his sin and fall, the judgment of death pronounced by God, and the great plan for man's salvation, which occupies such a large portion of the Book's teaching. But these same skeptics are hard put to it to find any scientific errors in this Book. The Word of God is never guilty of agreeing with the primitive science common to those who wrote contemporaneously with the Bible. Its aim is not to teach science, but there are many references to scientific matters. In every instance, this astonishing Record speaks with a calm certainty which is surprising. When the facts come to light, this Book is always shown to be correct.

I think we are justified, under these conditions, in paying strict attention to everything it has to say. This is especially true in connection with its warnings regarding the necessity of making provision for the sin which, as we know, according to the Book, condemns us all to an eternal death.

You, who listen to these broadcasts regularly, will know by this time that my purpose is not simply to educate or interest you in regard to the many fascinating features of God's world, but to get us acquainted with God, Himself. I know no better way than for us to examine His works. We seek His wisdom and power and unfathomable love in Creation, but we see these attributes also, and more markedly, in what He has done in order to restore fallen man to a place where we may enter the family of God, and have fellowship with God on equal terms with Jesus Christ.

Did I say, "on equal terms with Jesus Christ?" Yes, nothing less than that. You might imagine that to be impossible. At first glance that is how it appears, but remember we have an omnipotent God. Only He could discover a way whereby the entire race of mankind, doomed to death, could yet go free, and at the same time, satisfy God's justice. The whole concept, humanly speaking, is incredible and impossible. But we have a God of the impossible.

No wonder David breaks into song in the 95th Psalm, and in these words utters his praise of God:

> "Oh, come, let us sing unto the Lord, let
> us make a joyful noise to the rock of our
> salvation . . . for the Lord is a great God,
> and a great King above all gods. . . . Oh,
> come, let us worship and bow down; let us
> kneel before the Lord our Maker; for he is
> our God and we are the people of his pas-
> ture, and the sheep of his hand."

God had to find an infinite Substitute who would take the place of sinning and sentenced humanity. Who should it be? None other than Christ, Himself! Wonder of wonders—"Christ died for the ungodly. He was made sin for us, Who knew no sin, in order that we might be made the righteousness of God in Him."

Yes, His death on the Cross was not exemplary but substitutionary. He took my place; He took your place, so now you and I go free. Is that anything to you? It means much to me, thank God! What is keeping you from this wondreful Saviour? Why not make today— now—the time to say "yes" to Jesus Christ?

CHAPTER XV

GOD PLANTS A GARDEN

We shall now spend a few sessions learning some of the wonders of Plants. This is another wide field, and we cannot exhaust any of these realms. At present we are simply content to enter, and look around at a few of the marvelous things which catch our vision. We shall return again and again to continue our investigations.

It is interesting to note again the definite and logical order of creation, as recorded in the first chapter of Genesis. The beautiful and perfect creation of the first verse—"In the beginning God created the heavens and the earth,"—containing plants and animals, and existing for unknown ages, was destroyed by the tremendous cosmic cataclysm of the second verse— "and the earth became waste and void and darkness was upon the face of the deep." This catastrophe, obviously of stupendous character, suggests the first flood and possibly the beginning of the ice-age. It would appear to be the result of the Devil's hatred of God when he was thrown or "cast" to the ground, as we are informed in Ezek. 28:17.

In any case, there was stygian darkness and a world covered with water, torn and disordered by the mighty power of one who wished to destroy God's work. There is no reason to think that God would thus annihilate a beautiful world in which sin had not yet entered.

As light is necessary for all life, it is commanded to shine on the first day of this period of re-creation. It was a dim twilight, but was enough for God's purpose. On the second day, the earth's atmosphere was brought into existence, as we have noticed previously, and evaporation with all its possibilities appeared at the command of God, as well as the various other arrangements, which were necessary before life could survive.

On the third day, the continents of the earth were brought up from the ocean depths, as the water surged to the "storehouses" which the Creator had prepared for them (Psalm 33:7). Now it is time for vegetation to appear in all the varied forms which were to cover the ground.

> "And God said, Let the earth put forth grass, herbs yielding seed, and fruit trees bearing fruit after their kind, wherein is the seed thereof, upon the earth: and it was so. And the earth brought forth grass, herbs yielding seed after their kind, and trees bearing fruit, wherein is the seed thereof, after their kind: and God saw that it was good." (Gen. 1:11, 12.)

This botanical classification is remarkable for its simplicity and its up-to-dateness, the three great phyla mentioned including all that modern science knows. Science uses more ornate language and mentions four groups, which include the great number of simple plants, with and without chlorophyll, such as algae and fungi, up through the various forms until we come to Gymnosperms and Angiosperms, which are the most highly developed classes of the plant kingdom.

That Moses could have been so skilled in the science of botany as to write down correctly these facts on plant life, without the help of the Creator, is unthinkable.

That these various plants did not come from seeds, through an evolutionary process, long-drawn-out, is seen from Gen. 2:5:

> "And no plant of the field was yet in the earth, and no herb of the field had yet sprung up: for the Lord God had not yet caused it to rain upon the earth; and there was not a man to till the ground."

That means, obviously, that God, using His divine power, created the plants fully formed and placed them in the soil where they proceeded to grow and reproduce themselves precisely as they do today.

The loving thoughtfulness of our God is seen in the great variety of all kinds of vegetation, giving us such a wide assortment of grasses, woods, vegetables and fruits. It is also clearly recognized that He made provision for wide variations within the types but made it impossible for one kind to develop into another kind. All must reproduce "after its kind." This great Law effectively prevents the evolutionary changes which an infidel science, rejecting Creation, imagines must have taken place through long millions of years.

These acts of God were instantaneous: "He spake and it was done; He commanded and it stood fast." Wonderful Creator—the Lord Jesus Christ!

The strange powers conferred upon these living things, in order to insure their continuance by making possible wide distribution of seeds, and in many cases remarkable provision for the life of the seed, show again the inventive genius of our God, if we may speak in that way about the Creator's wisdom.

Plants are found wherever there is moisture and proper temperature. The presence of hot lava, excessive deposits of alkali or salt, and long-continued perriods of extreme heat or cold, are almost the only conditions under which vegetation will not thrive.

A bucket of water baled from the open sea may contain more tiny one-celled plants of the algae type than there are visible stars on a clear night. Even in the desert there are but few areas without plants of some variety. So-called "bare" rocks are partly covered with mosses and lichens. We may find them even high on the mountains close to perpetual snow. In the icebound interior of Greenland and the region of the poles, a tiny red plant, known as "red snow," dots the icy whiteness.

I have mentioned the four great groups. A few more details about these are in order. In Group or Phylum 1 containing the Algae and Fungi, there are more than 20,000 species of the former. Of these the most familiar are pond scums, kelps and rock weeds. In the Fungi series there are about 100,000 species. Among these are bacteria, molds, mildews, yeasts, smuts, rusts and mushrooms.

Phylum 2 contains about 20,000 species of mosses, and Phylum 3 about 5,000 species of ferns and their allies. Phylum 4 embraces all seeds and flowering plants and is the most important. In this group we find pines, firs, and spruces, etc., known as Conifers—500 species of them. Then, there are 30,000 species of what are known as Monocotyledons—grasses, palms, lilies, orchids, etc., with another 100,000 species of Dicotyledons—willows, walnuts, elms, roses, maples, potatoes, melons, etc.

Again we are face to face with Diety when we attempt to find an adequate explanation of this great number and variety in the plant kingdom. In the future talks, we shall consider the uses of plants as evidently designed by the Creator.

Jesus compared Himself to a plant when He said, as recorded in John 15:1, 2:

> "I am the true Vine and my Father is the Husbandman. Every branch in Me that beareth not fruit, He taketh away; and every branch that beareth fruit, He purgeth it that it may bring forth more fruit."

Here is pronounced a great Truth. There is a living Vine—Christ, and there are living branches. Some of these living branches—and they are all Christians— bear no fruit. The judgment upon them is not eternal death, but removal. They are "taken," not "cast" away. Then there are other branches of this Vine that do bear fruit. The Master or Husbandman, looking for an increased yield, is compelled to purge or prune these in order to cause them to produce more fruit.

Let us think of this for a moment—and I now speak to Christians who may be listening. You are connected with the Vine; you have life; but are you bearing fruit? If not, your state is a dangerous one. You may be "taken away," and your last opportunity to exalt the Saviour lost. He has long pleaded with you; you may have become careless and worldly, having lost your first love. Will you come back before He acts in judgment?

Then, many of you, who know the Lord and have served Him more or less faithfully, are in trouble of one kind and another. The burdens press heavily; you hardly know which way to turn for relief. You are wondering if God has forgotten to be gracious. Why does He permit you to suffer?

Well, remember the many comforting passages in God's Book. Listen!

> "Blessed is the man whom Thou chasten-
> est, and teachest him out of Thy law." (Ps. 94:12)
> "Whom the Lord loveth, He chasteneth,
> and scourgeth every son whom He receiv-
> eth. If ye endure castening, God dealeth
> with you as with sons; for what son is
> there whom his Father chasteneth not . . .
> but if ye be without chastening . . . then
> are ye not sons." (Heb. 12:6-8)

We Christians are the "planting of the Lord" and are safe for eternity, because we read in Matt. 15:13, the words of our Lord:

> "Every plant, which my heavenly Father
> hath not planted, shall be rooted up."

Conversely, then, every plant which has been planted by God shall never be rooted up. But what a disaster, if we are bearing little fruit and must be removed, thus losing our reward—even though we do gain heaven.

How blessed it is to "abide" in Jesus Christ. "He that abideth in Me and I in him, the same bringeth forth much fruit." (John 15:5)

Will you right now think of this question? Are you an "abiding" Christian, or are you one of those known as "carnal" Christians who look back on a day when Christ meant more than He does today? Do not permit anything to come between you and Him. If you do, you cannot grow because you are shut off from the Source of nourishment. Let us turn away from the world, and make Him supreme today.

> "Finally, my brethren, be strong in the Lord, and in the power of His might. Put on the whole armour of God, that we may be able to stand against the wiles of the devil. For we wrestle not against flesh and blood, but against principalities, against powers, against the rulers of the darkness of this world, against spiritual wickedness in high places.

> "Praying always with all prayer and supplication in the Spirit, and watching thereunto with all perseverance and supplication for all saints."

CHAPTER XVI

LITTLE STREAMS THAT RUN UPHILL

We continue our survey of some of the miracles of plants. For a moment think of their uses. Trees and other plants have many uses, one of the greatest perhaps, being the purification of the air. They take in the deadly carbonic acid gas, which is produced in great quantities in the breathing of animals, in decaying matter, and in burning materials. By a chemical process, the carbonic acid, or carbon dioxide, is used for the plants' own needs, and life-giving oxygen is released. Without this wonderful service of the plants, men and animals, along with every other form of life, would perish.

Plants play a large part in helping to beautify the world. They serve as food for man and beast. Many of them, also, are of untold value as medicine. Many of them provide shelter and raiment for humanity.

But you may be surprised to know that possibly the greatest service they render to our world is conveying the moisture of the earth into the atmosphere. Our world would soon become a desert if the trees were to be cut down.

The roots of trees are constantly bringing up water from below and discharging it through the leaves into the air. It is calculated that one large elm tree, through its leaves, evaporates as much water as the largest steam boiler, kept constantly boiling.

If a few cuttings of growing plants are placed in a basin holding about one-half pint of water, the water will be taken up and released by the plant in about twelve hours. So we see how manifold are their uses.

But this is not all. Besides serving as safeguards against drought, trees also afford considerable protection against floods and overflow. In some countries willows are planted to give stability to river banks. The roots of trees are invaluable in binding together the loose shifting soil of sand dunes and bars. Their foliage decays and helps to form a soil in which other trees and plants can live and thrive. Hillside trees fertilize the soil, hold back moisture that would otherwise escape, and afford protection from winds.

Plants provide an avenue for the greatest occupation of mankind—agriculture. Thinking only of the number of people and amount of capital employed, also of the use and value of labor to the world at large, agriculture, including forestry, goes far toward feeding, clothing and sheltering the world. It also supplies a great part of the manufacturing interests. These products are too numerous to be mentioned. With the discovery of plastics and all the varied products that can be produced from wood, we begin to see something of the wisdom of God in giving the earth such a magnificent supply of forests and vegetation.

Every plant is a living thing. It is provided with organs for taking in food materials, for breathing, for protection against its enemies, and for reproducing itself, in order to keep up the number of its own kind.

From the very beginning most plants are strugglers for food and room. Rapidly growing plants, like pigweed and ragweed, will soon crowd out and shade to death ordinary garden crops. Frosts, drought and floods destroy countless others. Plants are susceptible to diseases that are as catching as the mumps and the measles.

For every plant that succeeds in producing a crop of seeds, there are hundreds and thousands of failures. This also shows design and thoughtfulness when we think of what would happen if each seed belonging to a garden weed were allowed to bring forth its kind.

Higher types of plants are made of five very distinct parts—roots, stems, leaves, flowers, and fruit. These unite to form a factory for the production of seeds, and each has its own definite part in the job. It is not possible to study in detail these various parts, but we will look for a moment at one or two most interesting features.

It is impossible to understand the life processes of a plant without knowing something of the structure of roots. So necessary are roots that the Creator has given them most important functions. They must absorb water in large quantities—this water containing dissolved minerals which materials are used in the manufacture of starch and other products.

The roots anchor the plant to the ground, often growing deep into the soil, sometimes as far as fifty feet. It has been found that the roots under a two-year-old clump of prairie grass will stretch to about 319 miles. That means that the greater part of the plant is below ground.

The third use of roots is that of storing food, as in the carrot, turnip and beet.

The structure of a root shows beyond any doubt the wisdom of a Creator. It has a skin or epidermal covering in the form of a protective layer, just one cell in thickness. Its cell walls are made of thin, soft membranes of cellulose, which permit the absorption of water and dissolved mineral salts.

In order to secure a greater absorbing surface, roots are equipped with long, slender, delicate projections called root-hairs. Because of their great total surface area, and thin walls, they absorb most of the water admitted to the root. Also, they secrete an acid which aids in dissolving minerals.

In the central part or core of the root are found the conducting tubes for carrying the water, some transporting down from the leaf and others from the root upward—a beautiful system, intricate and accurate in its working.

Perhaps the greatest of all marvels is the chemistry of a green leaf. The leaves of a growing plant are arranged in such a way that they have the greatest possible exposure to the sun. There is little overlapping. Blades of grass are thin but grow very long, thus providing an increased area for catching the sun's rays. Plants cultivated indoors tend always to grow in the direction of light. The stems and leaf-stalks often twist about or grow to unusual lengths so that the leaves may receive the necessary sunlight. It is this sunlight which provides the energy for the vitally important process of food manufacture.

This astonishing process is known as photo-synthesis. Examine under the microscope the cut edge of a green leaf, and one sees little rooms with the tiny chlorophyll chemists doing their miraculous work. These small grains of chlorophyll, under the influence of the sun's energy, are combining the water drawn up from the ground by the roots, and the carbon dioxide drawn in from the air through thousands of wide-open mouths on the under side of the leaf. The water and carbon dioxide are brought together, and as the carbon is separated from the oxygen, the latter is released back into the atmosphere, while the carbon is used to make sugar, which is then changed into starch, so necessary for the life of animals and humans.

This process is not understood, so great is its intricacy, but without the strange power of the plant to use the sun's rays and the other materials, no life would be possible.

Not only do the plants return to us oxygen which is needed, but they give out much water into the atmosphere, thus in another way making life possible. Only a small part of the water absorbed by the roots is used by the plant in making the complex food substances, and the excess in the form of vapor is passed out through the leaf. It has been estimated that a tree of average size, on a warm day in summer, throws off nearly 1,000 pounds of water, and that the grass on a vacant city lot puts into the air about a ton of water in the same length of time.

Is it possible to know these things and believe there is no God? How right is Psalm 14! "The fool hath said in his heart, there is no God." Are you getting the Truth that these considerations are designed to press home? I trust that you are having a clearer vision of Creation and the Creator. I am sure of this, that if God becomes a real, living Personality in your life, your whole viewpoint will be changed. If you live from day to day, knowing there is a Supreme Being behind this world scene, working out a plan for nations and individuals, you will, if you are wise, want to know what that plan is, and then you will desire to fit yourself into it. Are you satisfied with your life up to this point? Have you taken Christ into your thinking, and have you given Him right-of-way? Such a decision will pay you infinite dividends. Why not invest in God today? One who has God is always equipped for every experience in life, no matter how dangerous and critical it may be. When you come to the place where there seems no way out, He can make a "way of escape." Annie Johnson Flint put it this way:

> "Have you come to the Red Sea place in
>   your life,
> When in spite of all you can do,
> There is no way out, there is no way back,
> There is no other way—but through?
> Then wait on the Lord with a trust serene,
> Till the night of your fear is gone;
> He will send the wind, He will heap the
>   floods;
> He says to your soul, Go on!
>
> And His hand will lead you through—clear
>   through—
> Ere the watery waves roll down;
> No foe can reach you, no wave can touch,
> No mightiest sea can drown.
> The tossing billows may rear their crest,
> Their foam at your feet may break;
> But over their bed you may walk dry-shod
> In a path that your Lord will make.
>
> In the morning watch, 'neath the lifted
>   cloud,
> You see but the Lord alone,
> Where He leads you on from the place by
>   the sea,
> To the land that you have not known,
> And your fears shall pass, as your foes
>   have passed,

You shall be no more afraid;
You shall sing His praise in a better land,
A place that His hand hath made."

Wonderful Saviour, isn't He?

CHAPTER XVII

ROOT MIRACLES

It is the business of roots to collect food materials and water from the soil, and to serve as anchors for holding the plant firmly in position. Roots are supposed to do their work underground, but there are many plants whose roots hang suspended in mid-air from the trunks of trees. Such are called aerial roots. They serve various purposes, chief among them being to absorb moisture and other useful substances from the air, and to take in water which drips from the branches above them. Thus the beautiful orchids of the tropics have aerial roots and sometimes they grow in the green-house. The ivy, too, has tiny aerial roots which act like tiny clutching fingers and help it to climb.

Do you know that growing corn has roots coming out from small swellings at some distance above the ground? These aerial roots then grow downward and outward into the ground, deciding to work in both ways—in air and in soil. So they serve the double purpose of bracing the stalk against the wind, and of supplying additional water from the soil. Some plants like the mistletoe have robber roots which bury themselves in other plants in order to steal the sap. Burglars! Yes, thieves in nature's garden.

All roots have their beginning in a seed. Suppose we examine a bean. We soak it to loosen the shiny covering and see how easily the hard part separates into two portions having two very small points. One of these will grow down into the ground, forming the root of the plant; the other will stretch up into the sunlight to form stem and leaves.

Cutting across a mature root we discover three distinct parts, the brown outer bark, the pale corky layer within this covering, and in the center the woody cylinder with ducts and vessels through which air and water travel. Near the tip we see two other distinguished features—the root hairs, and the root cap.

These root hairs are closed at the ends, are of countless numbers, and perform one of the most important works of the plant. As many as 480 root hairs have been counted on a small section of a corn rootlet, only one one-hundredth of an inch in length, grown in a very damp place.

The fibrous roots thrust their firm little points into the soil, drawing up water, potash, iron, and many other elements through their thin cell walls. Many of these delicacies are washed from the rocks and soil particles by means of a weak acid secreted by the hairs themselves. These chemical elements are mixed with the soil-water and passed on through the many ducts and passages to the stem itself, and thence upward to the chemical laboratory in the leaves.

The little root-caps are hard and close-fitting. There is no life in the outer portion but the inner part has active growing cells which renew the cap as it wears out. The root-cap is constantly being renewed and pushed ahead to open a channel through the soil. Here is Nature's diamond drill penetrating deep under ground. It never needs to be taken out or repaired; carries its own repair shop; recaps itself daily without shutting off the power for a moment. I think that is very interesting and wonderful.

As we have seen, roots go down into the ground much further than might be imagined. Winter wheat digs itself some seven feet into the earth. The roots of an oat plant, if cut off and strung from end to end, will measure about 150 feet. Oak trees have roots which extend out more than fifty feet from the tree.

Some plants, like the parsnip, beet, turnip, and carrot, store a great amount of nourishment in their roots. They are what are known as biennial plants—that is, they take two seasons to make seed. The first summer is given entirely to storing up plant food in the roots. In the second summer, if the root is planted, a stem shoots up quickly from the top of the root. It feeds upon the stored food and grows very rapidly, sending up a wealth of blossoms, which presently become veritable miracles of promise.

Many plants are grown directly from roots or root cuttings. A sweet potato or a dahlia root, if planted in damp sand, will quickly send up growing sprouts which spring from buds in the roots. Each sprout, if broken off and properly set out, will develop into a new plant.

Stems are most interesting things. They form the framework or body of the plant, and are of various shapes and sizes. In tropical forests where the shade is very dense, there are found many climbing plants, which run like great cables for hundreds of feet to reach the sunlight. All our early flowering plants like the snowdrop, the crocus, and the tulip, have richly stored underground stems.

In the desert regions there are many different kinds of cacti whose flattened stems serve for foliage. The thread-like leaves of the asparagus are really not leaves at all, but tiny branchs or stems, which do the regular work of leaves.

Stems of all kinds, short, long, large and small, have a definite job to perform. The precious soil-water with the various minerals, and all the nitrogen compounds used by the plant, must enter through the "doors" in the roots. Then it passes from roots to leaves which complete the chemical transformation into sugars and starches found in all the fruits and vegetables so much enjoyed by us. But how little thought we give to this miracle!

We have thought of the rising of the water or sap straight up through these tiny, hair-like tubes, moving slowly to the very top. These tubes are not joined together like water-pipes in a house. They are a series or chain of wood cells, like little oblong boxes piled end on end. A thin wall separates each cell from its neighbor, making the situation more wonderful from the standpoint of the onlooker. How does the sap ever get through, if there is no continuous and unbroken tube through which it can pass?

And do you know how sap gets from the ground to the topmost leaf on the tallest tree in the land? Well, this seems to be the explanation. The cell sap in the root hair is denser than the soil-water, so by a natural law which governs fluids, the soil-water seeps through the thin cell-wall and mingles with the sap in the root-hair. This extra amount of fluid naturally distends the tiny cell-chamber until it can hold no more. The sap fluid in this cell, now mixed with the dilute soil-water, is much thinner than the sap in the next or adjoining cell above. Following the same rule of attraction, the sap is drawn up into the denser cell, and so on and on, until it has mounted to the very topmost twig. Science is not certain as to the explanation of this mystery, but what I have given you seems the correct solution at the moment.

I must confess that this staggers me when I think of it. No one understands the process. It is beyond human skill to grasp its operation. Who but God could devise this plan?

Food comes down through the stem in one channel. Inside this is another channel which carries the liquid from the root up to the top. In addition to these uses, the stem provides storage for starch and sugar, needed in early spring time for the nourishment of flower buds and young leaves. Think of a sago palm yielding as much as 800 pounds of starchy material in a single trunk! Similar storehouses are found in the sweet potato, the dahlia and the gladiolus.

The thing that strikes us forcibly about all this is the immense care God has devoted to every detail, the small as well as the large. His work is perfect and complete. His plan for each plant is divine and mysterious, and under suitable conditions each plant will fulfill its destiny as the Creator ordered.

And here is a lesson for us. God has created us, not simply to satisfy a passing caprice. There is a plan for every life—God's plan. Unless we are careful to find this plan and put it into operation, we shall surely make shipwreck of our lives. Most people, obviously, are not interested in seeking to discover what God would have them be and do. In fact, it is the small minority, apparently, that is concerned even in God's existence. Mankind, with the bit in its teeth, drives madly to destruction, heedless of warnings from earth and heaven as to the dire results of disregarding God's plan for the world and for the individual.

This plan of God, whenever it has been tried, always works. No person who has found and carried out God's will has ever regretted it. Countless individuals come on the world's stage, live their brief span, and die like animals, without ever trying to get in vital contact with the Supreme Ruler of the Universe. And yet God has given us His Guide-Book in which He has laid down clearly and in considerable detail rules for every life.

These rules are clear-cut and understandable. They involve a recognition of God and Jesus Christ. This acknowledgment is not simply a mental assent to the fact that God and Christ exist. The Devil does that much and he is condemned.

In order to give God's plan a chance to work in my life, I must realize that I am a lost sinner, and that goes for every other man and woman. Being "lost" I am under sentence of death. This involves eternal and conscious punishment, and banishment from God's presence. That is a dreadful penalty but it is what God pronounces and I must believe it. God cannot lie. I admit I do not want to suffer this death penalty, if it can be avoided. And this is where God's plan fits right into my life. He tells me that He has accepted a Substitute for me, One who died in my place. That is easy to understand, and if true, changes the whole situation from one of utter hopelessness to one of glorious promise. Yes, Jesus Christ died, but there is just one thing I must do. I must come into personal contact with Him, and accept Him as my Saviour, making Him ruler of my life. Immediately, God tells me, I am free and now have become a child of God, one of His heirs, a joint-heir with Jesus Christ, the Son of God.

Does this plan work? It worked for me, my friend, and it has worked for millions of others, and we are not fooling ourselves. Don't you think it is at least worth a trial? I do, and I am asking you now to test it. Get alone with God, and then "get right with God." It means eternal life here and now. Will you try it?

CHAPTER XVIII

NATURE'S BAZOOKAS AMONG THE PLANTS

We are considering some of the wonders of plant life, and in this talk I ask you to think, among other things, of the strange and mysterious ways by which plants distribute their seeds. We can almost imagine them to be endowed with super-intelligence, and we are unable to resist the conclusion that here a Master Mind is at work.

In the blackberry and raspberry, for instance, the Engineer devised an indigestible pit around each seed. These pits permit the seeds to pass through the digestive canal in their original condition. A bear enjoying a meal of berries does not realize how helpful he is as a seed carrier. So animals are used ingeniously as an effectively operating transportation system for seeds.

Sometimes the rinds or seeds themselves are poisonous both to animals and men, and this serves as a warning. At other times the rind is simply unpalatable and discourages the marauder from penetrating further.

The mechanical devices adopted for the transportation of seeds are most striking. The tumbleweed with its feathery structure is able to roll along the ground for long distances. Carried by the wind the fruit breaks off and is deposited far from the parent plant.

Then, aeronautics is commonplace in nature. The Chinese Lantern is the familiar red plant used as an ornament in many modern homes. Its inflated calyx surrounds the fruit, which when it has ripened, is carried high into the air.

Winged fruits or seeds were the precursors of airplanes. The single-winged product of the ash, and the double-winged fruit of the maple, are so constructed that they will fly long distances in order to provide for germination away from the parent. The ailanthus bears a fruit which has a simple propeller.

The common milkweed and dandelion surprise us with their parachutes. The fruits bearing the seeds are wafted high in air and carried miles away from their birthplace.

Usually flowers use air currents for the transference of their pollen. If you doubt this, ask a hay fever sufferer! These pollen grains are very light-weight. In the case of pines, there is an appendage attached—a kind of air sac.

Many of our common native plants have mechanisms for releasing their seed—the envy of our modern engineers. The violet and columbine open their pods by means of valves, one to each pod from which the seeds spring with great force. The mustard plant splits its pods in a peculiar fashion, from the bottom upward, leaving behind a false partition, used for decorative effect. In some species this is beautifully dyed.

The evening primrose has a capsule which splits along four sutures, and from such a "trap" only a few seeds are allowed to escape at a time, thus insuring economy. The jimson weed or thornapple has a similar device.

The poppy, at the time of maturity, has small windows or pores at the apex of the capsule. As the wind moves the long stem of the plant back and forth, the very light seeds are blown out of the pods, a few at a time.

In plants like the jewel weed or touch-me-not, the seeds are forced out by spring-like gadgets. A slight jar causes the fruit to shoot its seeds quite long distances. The witchhazel also ejects its seeds with great force, sending them as far as twenty feet.

The lowly mushroom uses a spring to project its spores through the darkness to some small ray of light. Ferns scatter their spores by means of trigger-like devices on the under side of their fronds. The wild geranium uses a catapult to distribute its seeds. Each of the five seeds has its own private mechanism.

The squirting cucumber of southern Europe is very curious. Its fleshy fruit hangs from a stalk which acts as a stopper at one end. As the fruit matures, the cork-like plug pulls loose and the seeds are shot out with great violence because of the internal pressure accumulated throughout the growing season. In America, the wild balsam apple, a climbing annual, follows a similar plan.

Do you know that some plants are confirmed meat-eaters, and insist on a diet consisting of the bodies of their animal friends and acquaintances, and so these insect-eating plants must have a special device? Usually they are provided with a spring-like mechanism. Familiar examples are the pitcher plant, the sundew and the Venus' flytrap.

The pitcher plant has modified leaves forming a structure which resembles a pitcher and collects rain water. The plant nectar sweetens this water, making it attractive to insects. On the inside of the pitcher which is open at the top, there are stiff hairs pointing downward. The thirsty insect enters the pitcher, takes its drink and prepares to leave, but finds the way blocked by the hairs and is drowned. The plant now enjoys its meal leisurely.

The sundew is provided with tiny hairs on the upper surface of its leaves, the hairs secreting a sticky substance from glands located on their tips. This liquid looks like dew, but when the insect alights on it to enjoy the morning dewdrop, it gets the surprise of its short life. It is stuck fast. The hairs then bend toward the middle of the leaf, which closes and traps the insect, and that is the end of this particular bug. The sundew relishes its meal.

The leaves of the Venus' flytrap have two halves hinged together. On the surface of the leaves are hairlike structures which act like triggers. When the worm or fly crawls over these tiny bristles, an immediate impulse is carried to the leaves, resulting in instant closure of the leaves, their hinges permitting this remarkable response.

The sensitive plants, such as the common mimosa, close their compound leaves in mechanical fashion as the result of excessive heat, shock, or the onset of darkness. The huckleberry shoots its pollen from double-barreled shotguns.

Some pollen grains are rough or adhesive, causing them to adhere to the body or hairs of insects and animals. The stigmas of most flowers are made sticky in order to catch and hold in place the pollen, allowing it to germinate.

Some common weeds distribute their seeds by supplying them with tiny hooks which cling to the hair or fur of animals. Examples are the cocklebur, the common burdock or "sticker," with which most of us have had trouble one time or another, the bur marigold or beggar's tick, and the trefoil or "stick-tight." Each of these has hooked or barbed prongs and is loosely attached to the parent plant at maturity. Contact with some animal easily pulls it out and it is given a "free ride."

Coconuts, palm nuts, Solomon's seal, and many other fruits prefer water transportation and are so constructed that they will be safely carried to some distant shore without sinking.

Let us ask again—"Who but God could devise such an amazing array of unique devices as we have enumerated?"

So we see that Nature has many ways of giving the seeds a ride and free transportation to some unknown destination. This is a day of travel. People everywhere are on the move and we cross land and sea and fly through the air for long distances, often at great speed. This speed is one of the striking features of this twentieth century. Many centuries ago a strange prediction was given to Daniel, the great seer of Babylon, when he was an old man, probably about 90 years of age. This man of God—one of the most remarkable who ever lived—was given a glimpse into the distant future, and saw certain world-shaking events of our time.

He was anxious to know the date of these occurrences—quite a natural curiosity. But the angel would tell him little beyond saying that "at the time of the end, many shall RUN to and fro." This appears to indicate a marked increase in the speed of transportation just before the end of this age.

One thing is certain, the world has gone mad after speed; and if this is what was suggested by the angel, we are now living in exciting days. Tremendous events are in the offing—events of which we shall have something to say in later broadcasts.

Thinking of travel another of God's prophets took a strange ride one eventful day in the long ago. This man was Elijah and the story is told in 2 Kings, the 2d chapter.

> "There appeared a chariot of fire, and horses of fire . . . and Elijah went up by a whirlwind into heaven."

Some day I'd like to ask Elijah about that trip.

Another servant of God, Enoch, considerably older than Daniel—in fact 365 years of age, was taken by God and lifted bodily from earth to heaven as recorded in Gen. 5:24.

> "Enoch walked with God and he was not for God took him."

And shortly after the crucifixion of Christ, Philip the evangelist, after doing some personal work with an Ethiopian eunuch in the desert, and having no means of transportation back to civilization, was given a trip on God's Fast Express. This is what we read in Acts 8:39:

> "The Spirit of the Lord caught away Philip . . . but Philip was found at Azotus"

not very far from the city of Samaria which he had left a few days before.

Our Bible tells us that one day a vast host of people are to be given free heavenward transportation and will be "caught up" to "meet the Lord in the air." The brief reference is found in Paul's first letter to the Thessalonians and is of sensational interest.

When this possibility is mentioned, however, it is commonly greeted with expressions of incredulity. Eyebrows are raised and people take a second look, as if something is wrong mentally with us. It is difficult to understand this skeptical attitude. We cannot deny God the right to take His children to Himself in His own way. He is not restricted to our crude methods of transportation. If He can empower a lowly squirting cucumber, enabling it to shoot its seeds into the air, surely He can do greater things for us when He wills it. Is there anything illogical or childish or fanatical about this idea? I do not see it that way.

We are told that many people will be left on earth when this separation takes place, because only those who have accepted Christ as Saviour will be taken. I know I shall be "caught up." Why am I sure? It is not because I deserve this honor, but because I have linked myself to Jesus Christ. Have you done so yet? Better think about it, and decide to go along with us to the home in the sky.

CHAPTER XIX

COZY BEDS FOR TINY SEEDS

The wonders of plant life are not over when summer is past. Some of the most remarkable features are seen when the leaves fall in the autumn. We look at a tree from which dead leaves are dropping to the ground and we feel a tinge of sorrow. Here is the end of life for thousands of lovely bits of foliage, but the tree itself has been making preparations for another season. It is not so concerned with its present apparently dying condition, as with preserving its beauty and vigor until next spring time when it will burst forth again into fresh beauty and power.

And this brings us to something which is truly astonishing and usually unnoticed. I am thinking of buds —winter buds—which are already in place before the leaves fall. Break off, if you will, a leaf from the shining willow and look closely at the base of the leaf stalk, using a magnifying glass preferably. What you see will be something you will not forget.

Right at the spot where the leaf was broken off, you will notice a tiny bud enclosed in a single wrapping, which is an ideal example of Nature's way of doing up a parcel. This wrapping consists of two small leaves, joined at their margins, which exactly fit into each other. You may, if you are careful, strip off this wrapping in one piece by using a needle. Then with your magnifying glass examine what the wrapper contains. Here are five or six of NEXT year's leaves, absolutely perfect, even to the branching veins and the delicate toothing at the edges. There is a space between these miniature leaves, which cannot be detected with the naked eye.

When the spring sunshine gives its warmth to these midget leaves, they will speedily grow to their full size, becoming a beautiful spray. These inner leaves surround the precious flower cluster. If you pull off a sumach leaf, a drop of milky fluid immediately fills the wound you have made, but when this is wiped away, you see a little swelling, small and pale. It is next year's leaf bud. The honey locust covers its three or four baby leaf buds with a diminutive fur-lined chamber.

Of course, since all the tree's possibilities for the future are in these winter buds, the tree guards them most carefully. Each little package is wrapped in layers of scales, securely gummed together, and over this is laid a coat of varnish, to keep it safe from the weather. As a further precaution, some buds are carefully lined with fur, others with cotton-like hairs. All are very snug and warm in their cradles.

Sometimes instead of scales, a little brown cap is fitted snugly over the bud, as in the sycamore tree. Every one has seen the pussy willow's leathery hood, made in one piece and lined with a silvery fur. Wild cherry buds are slender and pointed, each sitting upon a small shelf. Butternut buds also have a shelf made for them and display a hairy ridge something like eyebrows. Black walnut buds are clothed in rich gray velvet.

Does the tree design these wonders for itself? To ask the question is to answer it. There is Some One behind everything we have been examining, and that Some One is God.

The leaf arrangement in all these buds of the various trees shows much diversity and yet definite plan and design. The leaves on an apple bud are set, one at a joint, on alternate sides of the twig. A line joining them is a spiral that goes twice around the twig before the sixth bud is reached directly above or below the one chosen for a starting point. This is known as the five-ranked order and is the plan adopted by the common fruit trees.

There are many leaf plans from two to thirteen and even more, the object being always to secure the best possible exposure to the sun and air.

In the early springtime when leaves and blossoms unfold, there are wonders in your garden that would seem to be possible only in Arabian Nights tales. Will you take time off next spring to watch the hepaticas as they poke their furry hoods up through the cold ground? They do not seem to mind the temperature, and no matter how the blustery March winds blow, they soon throw back their hoods, and out come dainty flowers of pink, and lavender, and white. We see, if we look carefully, on each bush and tree, the marvels of Nature's careful packing. As the breezes gradually shake out the wrinkles, we discover that some leaves have been rolled, like a sheet of music in its case, or like a window-shade around its roller.

Some have been folded like fans, others doubled, length-wise down the middle. May apple leaves look like closed umbrellas, and open out just as you open an umbrella.

Usually the manner of folding concerns the shape of the leaf. The baby leaf of the tulip tree looks as if its tip had been clipped out with two snips of a pair of scissors. The creases show how, as it slept in its bud, it was folded lengthwise down the middle, and then bent over on its stalk, until its green blade was upside down.

We are told by scientists that the toothing and pointing of leaves is in order to provide various little "tongues" for grasping and holding the rays of the sun. In Europe where there is more moisture and less sunshine than here, the leaves are much more notched than ours.

If you look on a hot summer day when the sun's rays are very penetrating, you will see that the leaves are poised edgewise to the sky. This tends to keep the leaf from becoming parched and withered.

In the southwestern part of the states is a curious plant known as the compass flower or pilot weed, which cleverly avoids the hot rays by pointing its leaves north and south, and training them edgewise to the sky.

No wonder that Longfellow wrote in Evangeline:

> "'Patience,' the priest would say, 'have faith and thy prayer shall be answered.
> Look at this delicate plant, that lifts its head from the meadow.
> See how its leaves all point to the north, as true as the magnet.
> It is the compass flower, that the finger of God hath suspended
> Here on its fragile stalk, to direct the traveler's journey
> Over the sea-like, pathless, limitless waste of the desert.
> Such, in the soul of man, is faith.'"

So wrote Longfellow.

An old philosopher once exclaimed: "What a thought that was when God thought of a tree!" Yes, this is true. Any tree is a thought of God, originating in an atom of seed, deriving its vitality from heaven, its juices from the earth, its food from the air, its color from the sunbeam, and manufacturing its several parts by the mysterious power of its own vitality.

Here is a concourse of contrivances and properties and functions such as never would have entered the mind of man had not God set it in living form before him.

What must our conception be of the unerring Mind that contrived a hundred thousand contrasting plants and trees, differing in their size from the invisible lichen of the naked rock to the enormous banyan tree of India, large enough to shelter beneath its shade an army of men; differing in their age limits from the ephemeral "flower of the grass," to the mighty Redwood of California, which if it could speak, might tell us of events which transpired 5,000 years ago. Trees differ in the structure of their roots, in the form of their leaves, in the texture of their stems, in their flowers, seeds and fruits, in the rapidity of their growth, in their circulation and decay, in their manner of absorbing and reflecting the heat of the sun, and in a multitude of other particulars. In this kingdom we behold a diversity which is almost endless.

Turning our attention from this aspect to the divine Mind, responsible for it all, we know that in this Mind must have been a vast storehouse of glorious ideas and designs, the plans perfect and complete, before the omnipotent command went forth to clothe the earth with verdure. No difficulty was unsurmounted, no part of the divine purposes failed, no tree or plant or blade of grass came short of its designed perfection.

Is there any wonder then that on the evening of that glorious Third Day of creation, God pronounced all His work very good? But God would have us learn other lessons besides the wisdom and might of His creative power. In Matt. 6:28-34, Jesus brings to us a great Truth when He spoke these words:

> "Why are ye anxious concerning raiment? Consider the lilies of the field how they grow; they toil not, neither do their spin; yet I say unto you that even Solomon in all his glory was not arrayed like one of these.
>
> But if God doth so clothe the grass of the field, which today is, and tomorrow is cast into the oven, shall He not much more clothe you, O ye of little faith?
>
> BE NOT THEREFORE ANXIOUS, saying, What shall we eat? or, What shall we drink? or, Wherewithal shall we be clothed?
>
> For after all THESE things do the Gentiles seek; for your heavenly Father knoweth that ye have need of all these things. But seek ye first His kingdom and His righteousness; and all these things shall be added unto you.
>
> Be not therefore anxious for the morrow: for the morrow will be anxious for itself. Sufficient unto the day is the evil thereof."

Is it possible for us to arrive at a place in life

where all anxiety is unknown? Can we in any way discover and appropriate this security and peace of mind which nothing can destroy? If such an attainment is possible, it seems to me that it is one of the most desirable of all quests.

How may we get to this place of restfulness and constant supply of our needs? The way our Lord speaks of it, it is very simple. Listen.

> "Come unto me, all ye that labor and are
> heavy laden, and I will give you rest."

Today I'm taking Him at His word, and I'm glad to tell you I've found the promised rest. It is for you, too. Many of you are rejoicing in this now. Many of you long for it, but have not yet carried out the one condition. You must fall at His feet, and take Him as Saviour. Why not, just where you are at this moment, bow and surrender? You will never regret it.

CHAPTER XX

PLANT CHEMISTS AND FLOWERS THAT ADVERTISE

We shall think today of the wonder-working chlorophyll chemists in the green leaf. This chemical laboratory performs amazing feats of skill, its chief business being to make starch for plant food. What remarkable food this is! From it comes not only wood, but cork, and the tender petals of flowers, the flesh of fruits, and the widest variety of gums, oils, essences, and perfumes.

These hard-working leaves accomplish an invaluable service to mankind, a service which has been previously mentioned: the imprisoning of the deadly carbonic acid gas and the releasing of oxygen which purifies and renovates the atmosphere. All this machinery is compressed between the very thin leaf walls.

Let us examine a leaf. We find that the leafy skeleton is divided into a network of woody threads. These threads or veins connect with larger ones in the leaf-stalk, and these in turn are joined to veins in the branch.

Filling in the spaces between the network, is a green pulp, somewhat resembling a honeycomb. It is made up of a row of cells, each cell a little bag of transparent skin, filled with a colorless jelly.

This jelly is itself clear, but is so full of floating particles of vivid green that the entire leaf has this bright color. These green specks are the chlorophyll chemists. They are the machinery of the laboratory.

Over this network of cells there is a transparent leaf-skin. The purpose of this skin is to prevent the sun from drying up the juices in the leaf. So smooth and polished is the leaf skin of most leaves that they shed water like tiny umbrellas.

The water, which is constantly rising from below through the roots, must evaporate easily; otherwise the starch factory would soon overflow. So, to aid in evaporation, the under sides of the leaves have thousands of wide-open mouths, little pores or stomata, for the easy passage of air and vapor. Inside every leaf, then, proceed all the complex activities which make life possible.

The name which is attached to these operations of the leaf is rather a large one, photosynthesis. It means that when sunlight falls upon the green plant, the chlorophyll particles snatch the rays, which supply them with energy, and by some unknown sleight-of-hand they combine the carbon dioxide, which comes to them through the air, with the water which arrives chiefly from the roots, thus bringing into being sugars and starches. These sugars and starches are carbohydrate foods, and later, part of these are changed by the plants into fats and proteins. Fats, like starches and sugars, are composed only of oxygen, hydrogen and carbon. Proteins consist of these three elements, combined with nitrogen, sulphur, iron, potassium, and many other elements.

So, we can understand something of this vast business of photosynthesis as we sum up the process. The leaves have, as their source of energy, the sun. The raw materials used are soil, water and carbon dioxide from the air. The manufacturing plant is made up of leaves and the bark of young stems. The operating machines or the skilled chemists are the thousands of chlorophyll bodies. The transportation system within the factory is made up of the intricate series of vascular bundles for the passage of fluids up and down. The product is carbohydrates, chiefly starch and sugar. The by-product is oxygen which is thrown off and used by mankind.

In all this we observe a system so complicated and exact that the mind of man is baffled by the mystery of it.

Before plants can be fertilized and able to propagate themselves, the pollen dust must reach the pistil which lies at the bottom of the flower. It is the business of the pistils to form seeds, and to nourish and shelter them until they are ready to be sent out to the world, but this cannot be done until the pollen reaches its destination. When the pollen dust falls on the sticky stigma, it is firmly held. This tiny speck of pollen dust now bores a tube down inside the style and enters the ovary. Then, a small bit of protoplasm slips down the pollen tube and mixes with the substance in the little seed beginning. Immediately the baby seed is formed and begins to grow.

God devised a curious and altogether marvelous plan whereby pollen dust would be carried to the proper destination and reach its appointed place safely. He called upon the insect world to undertake the job. The bees are the chief agents, and naturally, the Creator, wishing to bring them to the flowers, gave the flowers color and fragrance as definite attractions, along with

a tiny drop of sweet fluid, which would reward their
visit to the bottom of the flower. In return for the
flowers' nectar, the bees thus act as faithful messen-
gers, carrying the pollen from flower to flower.

The more we look into blossoms, the more we realize how wisely this business has been planned. If all
the trees depending on insects, blossomed at once, some
would certainly be neglected. And so it is, there is a
definite and regular order. On one tree, the blossoms
are just peeping forth; on another the seeds are set;
still another has both fruit and seed fluttering here
and there; a fourth is in the full glory of leaf foliage
with blossom time and seed-sowing all but forgotten.
Here again is design.

Some flowers and plants have advertising cards or
signs which insects have no difficulty in reading. The
red clover blossom is made up of quite a number of
separate parts, each known as a floret. The bees know
which florets contain nectar; and this is how they know
it. If one of the florets has been drained and the seed
set, the seed vessel closes over, and the floret turns
brown and hangs downward. This brown signal says,
"No admittance," and the bee promptly passes along
to another. When all the florets in a head have been
fertilized, the head is brown and crumpled, endeavoring
to look as unattractive as possible to such enemies as
might suspect the presence of the little seed-treasures
at the bottom of the florets, and feast upon them.

It seems to be the perfume of the flowers rather
than the color which attracts the insects. These insects
have a keen sense of smell—much keener than their
vision—and can detect odors quite imperceptible to us.

Floral structure seems to determine what type of

creature can be accommodated. In regions where the trumpet vine flaunts its orange bloom, the humming bird will almost stand on its head in the horn; some of the flowers are pollinated by slugs; aquatic plants have water-borne pollen. Flowers which bloom at night are nearly always white and sweet scented. Red, violet, and blue are the colors which are most attractive to bees and butterflies. Dull yellow, brownish, and dark purple flowers seem to depend largely on the visits of flies.

All these interesting facts show that wherever we touch plant life we are near to the great Creator. Every individual plant, and vegetable, and tree is the special work of God. They neither weave, nor spin, nor paint themselves. Beholding them, we see God, Himself, patiently and unremittingly at work. He is present with every flower that springs up in the garden, or the field, or the wilderness, and gives to it with His own hand every one of its leaves, and every tint that contributes to the beauty of its coloring. He presides over it from the first impulse of germination to the last moment of fading existence.

How natural then for us to believe that, if He thus cares for each blade of grass, much more will He care for those whom He has created in His own image. Some of you listening today are in trouble. It may be that bereavement has come to your home and a loved one has been taken. You prayed God to spare that life, and you are disappointed and perhaps a bit rebellious. You are tempted to turn away from God because this sorrow has been permitted. Do not forget the lesson we tried to learn the other day, that "Whom the Lord loveth He chasteneth, and scourgeth every son whom He receiveth."

I have discovered that the people who go through life without trouble and sorrow usually are not the ones who have fine and attractive characters. It takes the crises of life to bring us close to the Father's arms. So, whatever your condition, know that God never makes a mistake.

Every green thing that springs out of the ground has something to say to us. All the leaves of the forest join in one general murmur to repeat in our ears the prophet's warning, "We do all fade as a leaf." We are apt to thrust this truth out of our minds, but in order that we may not forget, every autumn when the fading-time comes, God spreads before us on plain and hillside, a great parable in which our own decay and death are pictorially represented so vividly that all may read and reflect. Someone has put it like this:

> "Like leaves on trees the race of man is
>   found,
> Now green in youth, now withered on the
>   ground;
> Another race the following age supplies;
> They fall successive, and successive rise;
> So, generations in their course decay;
> So flourish these, when those have passed
>   away."

When you and I reach the end of the trail, what will it be—endless joy with Christ or eternal punishment with the lost? I hope no one listening today will fail to take advantage of God's offer of a free and perfect and present salvation.

Why hesitate any longer? Why not exercise your will, break away from that indecision, and say to Jesus Christ, "I'm taking Thee as my Saviour." If you will, a glorious surprise awaits you.

CHAPTER XXI

GOD AND NATURE

During several recent broadcasts we have been directing our attention to the wonders of plant life. It has been a fascinating study and with this talk we shall conclude for the present our meditations on the miracles of the vegetable kingdom.

We might as well review briefly some of the things we have learned. Our survey has been very hurried and incomplete because in our walk through God's garden, we have simply glanced here and there for a moment at the beauties and marvels which have unveiled themselves before our eyes.

We have seen the botanical classification of plant life as it is written down in Genesis, and have found it to agree with our modern scientific ideas. We have thought of the almost infinite variety of stalk and leaf of flower and fruit among hundreds of thousands of species. We have seen the curious devices for getting food for growth and seed production. We have watched the way Nature provides for the wide dispersal of seeds across the earth, her mechanical devices of parachute and rocket gun antedating our modern discoveries by thousands of years.

We have gazed with awe at the downy beds in which lie the baby seeds, protected from dangers that would bring death and destruction. We have marveled at the mysteries of photosynthesis, and the skill of the chlorophyll chemists in their tiny leaf laboratories, turning carbon and water into all kinds of foods for the benefit of mankind.

One insistent question keeps thrusting itself forward: What is the explanation of the mystery of the operations undertaken and carried through so easily and accurately by these humble life forms? We have come to the conclusion that the most learned scientist in the universe is unable to offer up a satisfactory solution to our problem. These tiny particles of living protoplasm guard their secret well.

Many things we would like to know. For instance, whence originates that spark of life that brings super-human power and wisdom to these cells that divide and redivide with unerring precision. How do they build for themselves their snug and secluded cradles and at the same time extract a steady stream of nourishment from soil, water, and air, snatching at passing sun rays for the indispensable light without which nothing would be possible? We watch them bring sugars and starches from carbon and water, and stand amazed as we behold them delivering their products through leaf-stalk and branch to the luscious fruit somewhere along the line.

Who can cause us to understand anything about this? To say that it is nothing more than the working of a Law of Nature, is to use words without meaning. What is NATURE? Is it an entity? Does it possess Personality? Where does Nature dwell? Has it ever been seen? Wherever it is, how does it convey knowledge of this "Law" to millions of cells in all parts of the globe? How do the cells so instantly and perfectly understand the instructions, as they are delivered? Where do cells get the power to put into immediate operation, the innumerable details, taking every step in this very complicated process in the correct order? This order seems to be predetermined in every case. The slightest mistake would ruin the whole result, and yet there is never a misstep.

Is there a School where these cells may learn the mysterious plan whereby an infinitely small particle of protoplasmic life may multiply itself into countless billions of other cells, each cell knowing as much as its predecessors, and without excitement or confusion, completing the amazing work to a perfect end?

Who organized this School? Who is Headmaster? Where are the sessions held? What language is used? How long do the courses of study last? Are there any graduation exercises?

These and a hundred other questions press into our curious minds and demand an answer. We make inquiry from College and University, and interrogate world-renowned authorities in all the sciences, but to our anxious questioning they have no answer. The only sound we hear is the echo of our earnest query.

The same quest for the Source of wisdom is depicted in the 28th chapter of Job, where the writer draws attention to many of man's accomplishments, and to his fruitless search for the Prime Cause of it all. Job is interested in the acknowledged fact that man has been able to perform many notable deeds. He has penetrated some distance into the earth. He has brought up silver and gold and iron and copper through the deep shafts he has constructed into the interior.

Man's strength has enabled him almost to overturn mountains "by the roots" as he cuts out channels among the rocks. He can build dams which restrain the mighty torrents of water and makes many discoveries. But—and this is the mystery—"Where shall Wisdom be found and where is the place of understanding?"

After failing to discover the secret anywhere on earth, man decides that perhaps he can buy the information. So he estimates his financial resources, only to be told:

> "It cannot be gotten for gold, neither shall silver be weighed for the price thereof. It cannot be valued with gold of Ophir, with the precious onyx, or with the sapphire. . . . Yes, the price of wisdom is above rubies. The topaz of Ethiopia shall not equal it, neither shall it be valued with pure gold."

Seeing that the earth refuses to disclose anything, man decides to ask the ocean. "O mighty sea, can you tell me where Wisdom dwells?" But again:

> "The deep saith, it is not in me; and the sea saith, it is not with me."

A puzzled and disappointed earth-dweller has just one more place to go — the place of Death. In this region of doom and destruction is there any knowledge of Wisdom? What is the answer? Destruction and Death say: "WE HAVE HEARD A RUMOR THEREOF WITH OUR EARS."

This reluctant admission does not, of course, tell all that Death knows. "The last enemy that shall be destroyed is Death," we read, and this grudging acknowledgment and this reluctant admission that there may be a God are what we might expect from the last enemy.

But now God, Himself, steps into the discussion to make the great Revelation and to answer our question. So we read in Job 28:23-28:

> "It is God who understandeth the way thereof, and He knoweth the place thereof. For He looketh to the ends of the earth, and seeth under the whole heaven . . . He establish it, yea, and searched it out. And unto man He said, Behold, the fear of the Lord, THAT IS WISDOM; and to depart from evil is understanding."

And there is the answer, my friend. There is a God, a God who understands, a God who created heaven and earth, the Source of all things in the universe, inanimate and living, from starry worlds of immeasurable size to the microscopic infusorium with its infinite variety of accomplishments. This is He who made oceans and lakes and rivers, filling them with varied forms of life. This is the God who placed on the earth the thousands of forms of living things; birds, insects, animals, and man. He made the trees—and most amazing of all—His enemies slew Him on a tree. The Almighty Creator, Jesus Christ, hangs suspended between heaven and earth, helpless, and forsaken by man and God, because the sins of the world were all piled upon Him. He died for us, and—thank God—rose again, Conqueror over death and the grave, that we, through faith in Him, might have everlasting life.

This God, by His own affirmation, is a Gardener and Husbandman. He speaks of His children as: "The branch of my planting, the work of my hands, trees of righteousness, the planting of the Lord." (Isa. 60:21 . . . 61:3.) This planting is more precious to Him than the nineteen different kinds of trees mentioned in the Bible, and all the other products of His omnipotence.

Jesus often spoke of His followers, as trees and branches of the Vine, and mentioned their fruit-bearing. He tells us that we reveal ourselves by the kind of fruit we bear. "There is no good tree that bringeth forth corrupt fruit; nor again a corrupt tree that bringeth forth good fruit. For each tree is known by its fruit. For of thorns men do not gather figs, nor of a bramble bush gather they grapes." (Luke 6:43, 44.)

Let us for a moment think of ourselves as apple tree Christians. You are bearing fruit. What sort is it? Crab apples, sour and astringent and distasteful? Has anyone ever tasted your fruit, and gone away with a wry face, saying: "If that is the fruit of Christianity, I want none of it"?

Or, are you bearing Northern Spies, luscious and tasty? If this be your tree, I'm sure some have admired your product, and have tasted. Then, they may have asked you for a graft to put into their own tree. You have directed them to Jesus Christ, and now they belong to our family.

It's an exciting experience to be planted by the Lord and to have the privilege of bearing some fruit for Him. He provides us with everything—the water of life, the breath of life, and the sunshine, without which there can be no results.

Are your roots planted deep in Him today? Or are you buried in the world and worldly things, without any hope for this world or the next? Why not take the exciting step into God's garden and let Him give you new life and joy and peace?

CHAPTER XXII

SPOUTING WHALES

We shall spend several sessions now studying many of the tenants of our globe, in water and on land. We shall see many strange and fascinating animals and insects, birds and fish, and always we shall look beyond these varied forms of life to the Creator.

Let us read the Genesis account of their origin. The story is brief, only six verses in the first chapter:

> "And God said, Let the waters swarm with swarms of living creatures, and let birds fly above the heaven.

> "And God created the great sea-monsters, and every living creature that moveth, wherewith the waters swarmed, after their kind; and God saw that it was good. And God blessed them, saying, Be fruitful and multiply, and fill the waters in the seas, and let birds multiply on the earth. And there was evening and there was morning, a fifth day.

> "And God said, Let the earth bring forth living creatures after their kind, cattle, and creeping things, and beasts of the earth after their kind; and it was so. And God made the beasts of the earth after their kind, and everything that creepeth upon the ground after its kind; and God saw that it was good."

Here we have the creation of all living things that inhabit the water and that fly through the air: whales, fishes, birds and insects on the fifth day; and on the sixth day: cattle, beasts, and creeping things, including herbivorous creatures, the various species of tame and domestic animals such as sheep and oxen. The Carnivora animals are included under the name: beasts, lions, bears, etc. The creeping things embrace the reptile family: serpents, frogs, etc.

It will be noticed that God made each living creature, "after its kind," implying not only their variety of forms, instincts, and habits; but that each must produce its own kind, and its own kind only, through all successive generations. By this law of the Creator, any evolutionary transmutation of species would seem to be impossible.

It would require many volumes to study all the varied forms of animal life placed in our world, so we select only a few from each class for examination. In each of them we shall discern without difficulty the wisdom of the Creator.

The whale family includes not only the animals commonly designated by that name, but also the grampus, porpoise, dolphin, etc. They are remarkable creatures. Like fish they live in the water, but all their internal parts resemble those of land animals. They have lungs, liver, spleen, bladder and a heart with partitions, pumping red blood throughout their bodies. They breathe air, and are viviparous—that is, they bring forth living young like other mammals, and suckle their young.

The Cetacea, which is the Order to which whales and dolphins belong, include the largest of all mammals. They are more thoroughly aquatic than the seals. They obtain their livelihood in the waters, and their entire structure fits them for traversing the waves.

Although the whales closely resemble fish, and are able to pass a considerable time below water, they possess no gills, but must breath atmospheric air as do other members of the mammal family.

When one of these gigantic creatures rises to the surface of the sea, it makes huge respirations, called "spoutings," in which a column of mixed water and vapor is ejected from the nostrils or blow-holes to a height of as much as twenty feet. The blow-holes are placed in the upper part of the head so that it is necessary to have only this part of the body out of the water when breathing. In order that this animal may descend into the depths and remain there for a considerable time without getting fresh supplies of air, it has a very large reservoir of arterial blood which receives oxygen during the spoutings and is kept in reserve for use by the four-chambered heart. Of course, there is a large lung capacity also, and the whale draws on this supply of oxygen. When its reservoir is exhausted, it must rise to the surface or drown. The fore limbs look very much like fins of fish, but on close examination they are seen to have fingers or digits typically mammalian. These fins are not of much help in progression. The whale moves by means of a horizontal and enormously powerful tail. The front limbs are used to preserve the balance of the huge mass, and the mother whale uses them as arms to clasp her offspring.

Usually there is just one young whale at birth. It is born alive and suckled like other young mammals; also it is immediately able to accompany its mother in her path through the waves.

The skin of the whale is hairless, and underneath is a large layer of fat, sometimes nearly two feet in thickness, elastic as india-rubber, and providing warmth and resistance to the enormous pressure of the water when the body is deeply submerged. It is said that whales can plunge to a depth of 4,000 or 5,000 feet where the pressure is about 200,000 tons. Here again is design.

These whales are the most gigantic animals in the world. The elephant and rhinoceros are pigmies in comparison. The Cachalot or Sperm whale often attains a length of sixty or seventy feet, while the common whale has been found more than 100 feet long, and weighing more than 250 tons.

The spinal column is like the trunk of a good sized tree, the individual veretbrae being massive blocks bound together by the toughest ligaments and cartilages. The main artery is a pipe large enough to hold easily a full grown man.

The heart is a great engine of stupendous capacity and power, throwing out gallons of blood at every pulsation. The mouth is large enough to engulf a boat with all its crew, its tongue like a vast feather bed where a half dozen men could lie. Its flattened tail as a massive plate of a hundred square feet of marvelous strength, able with one blow to dash to pieces the stoutest boat.

The Greenland whale, Northern whale, or Right whale, is an inhabitant of the Arctic Ocean. Its head is remarkably large; the jaws opening very far back, the mouth about sixteen feet in length, seven feet in width, and ten or twelve feet high. Into this cavernous opening a good sized boat might enter.

The most curious feature of the mouth is the baleen, several hundred plates of which hang down from each side of the upper jaw. These strips vary in length according to position, but the largest are from ten to twelve feet long, nearly a foot wide at the base, and splitting at the extremity into a multitude of hairy-like fringes. The total weight of the baleen in a large whale is about a ton.

When feeding, the animal drives along with mouth wide open, engulfing countless millions of tiny beings that swarm in the waters—small shrimps, crabs, lobsters, molluscs, etc. When the mouth is filled with this mass of living creatures, the tongue weighing two tons, is raised, then the water is strained out through the baleen fringes, leaving a mass of food to travel down the gullet, which is so small that the largest whale in the world cannot swallow a good-sized herring. Can we resist the inference that this arrangement for feeding must have been planned?

In spite of its huge size and enormous bulk, this species of whale is inoffensive and timid, except when roused by pain or the sight of its offspring in danger, and will always flee the presence of man.

The words of the Lord are perfect, and all serve to extol His wisdom and power and goodness. Even the huge frames of these leviathans of the ocean display the perfection of workmanship.

Every member and organ, every fibre of the muscles that wield their ponderous body, every vein and artery concerned in driving the vital fluid through the immense bodies, and every nerve and tissue down to those that can be seen and examined only by the aid of a microscope; they are all finished with a delicacy and perfection that are inimitable and unsurpassed.

How clearly we see the hand of the Creator in His dealing with these monsters. He has given them affection for their young and for their kind, and they manifest a faithfulness to one another which often surpasses the love of humans.

They are faithful to the instinctive laws which have been made for them, and to such a degree that humans could learn much from them of conjugal fidelity and parental love. Two whales, male and female, will remain faithful to one another throughout their lives, and show great delight as they play in the water hoisting their bodies into the air, spouting and splashing in a great display of good nature.

We join with the writer of Psalm 104 and say, in reverent praise: "O Lord, how manifold are Thy works. In wisdom hast Thou made them all: the earth is full of Thy riches. Yonder is the sea great and wide, wherein are things creeping innumerable, both small and great beasts. There go the ships; there is leviathan whom Thou hast formed to play therein. THESE WAIT FOR THEE, that Thou mayest give them their meat in due season. Thou givest unto them, they gather; Thou openest Thy hand, they are satisfied with good; Thou hidest Thy face, they are troubled; Thou takest away their breath, they die, and return to their dust. Thou sendest forth Thy Spirit, they are created; and Thou renewest the face of the ground. The glory of the Lord shall endure forever; the Lord shall rejoice in His works."

Repeatedly, the Bible brings evidence to show how wonderful are the attributes of God in creation. If this aspect of the Almighty is so important in God's sight, surely we must not neglect to examine it. If our minds are open, there can be but one result. We shall be impelled to worship such a loving and powerful heavenly Father. We shall not be content to hold merely a cold intellectual view of Him. We shall not be satisfied simply to admire His greatness in making this world. We shall go further and understand His relationship to us and ours to Him.

If we are as wise as we ought to be, we shall sit at His feet and learn, sit in submission and surrender, acknowledging our sin, but gladly accepting the sinner's Friend, the Lord Jesus Christ, as our perfect Saviour.

If you disagree with this conclusion, will you not write me and tell me your reason? If you agree, God bless you, and I'll be glad to hear from you, too, so that we may fellowship together in this faith which is our greatest possession.

CHAPTER XXIII

MORE ABOUT WHALES

We have just begun a series of studies in the Animal Kingdom, and in the preceding talk, we looked first at whales, for no particular reason, except that, as they are the largest forms of animal life now known to exist, they seemed to demand notice.

Whales, porpoises, and dolphins belong to the order Cetacea; and all are recognizable by the entire absence of hind limbs. Deep within the body wall, however, are found small pieces of bone which seem to have no use, and those who believe in the evolutionary theory are fond of saying—without reason, I think—that these pieces of bone are remnants of hind limbs which were present when these creatures lived on land and were what we call terrestrial animals. We shall not argue the point at this time, although it may be said that here is a reasonable explanation of this phenomenon.

Whales, although so large and powerful, are thought not to live to a great age, which is contrary to the general rule among large mammals. A female member of this tribe will produce young as early as three years —one at a birth.

While showing great differences in size, whales and dolphins have many features in common. The porpoise is only four or five feet in length and weighs about sixty pounds. The Sulphur Bottom whale grows to be 100 or more feet long and weighs many tons.

The head of the whale, although possibly enormous,

is relatively light in weight. The brain is large and shows many convolutions, but the senses of smell and hearing seem to be slight. The nostrils are placed at the top of the head to form the well-known "blow-hole" which can be closed by a powerful valve.

Teeth may be huge and numerous, or may be altogether absent. The tail, flattened into two horizontal paddles or "flukes" of fat and muscle, provides most of the motive power, propelling the animal with an "up and down" motion as opposed to the "side to side" motion seen in all fishes.

The Whalebone whales comprise the Right whales and the Grey whales. Both show what was described in the last broadcast, the baleen which consists of long strands of horny substance hanging down for a distance of several feet, forming a curtain-like sieve, which strains off the sea water and separates the small forms of life by the thousands, on which the whale lives.

The Spulphur Bottom is a giant among giants, and attains a length of 100 feet or more—the largest mammal now living. An adult African elephant, eleven feet high at the shoulder, could stand quite comfortably inside it. Most whales are fond of company and so travel in herds, as do the miniature species in what are called "schools."

Many of them show great speed and activity, especially the Humpback whale which, in spite of great length and immense weight, indulges in a grotesque courtship, leaping high out of the water like a tarpon or salmon, apparently just showing off before its spouse.

The Cachalot or Sperm whale is of particular interest. It usually inhabits the warmer parts of the ocean and travels from one part of the globe to the other. Whales caught in the Atlantic Ocean have been found with spears of South Pacific islanders embedded in their flesh. Some of these animals have a circumference of thirty to forty feet, and when they were more common than now, doubtless many exceeded these dimensions.

The distinguishing feature of the Cachalot is its enormous and curiously formed head, in the upper portion of which is a great cavity, containing a transparent liquid, a mixture of oil and spermaceti. When purified and hardened it is used as a medicinal ointment, and for the manufacture of candles. A whale sixty feet long may yield about twenty-five barrels of spermaceti and 100 barrels of oil.

There is found, in addition, a still more valuable substance, ambergris, which is a fatty concretion of the bile ducts. It exists in small quantity in the intestines of the whale, but is usually found floating in the sea, where it has been ejected in large masses, sometimes a hundred pounds in weight. Refined ambergris is an expensive drug, and is used in making costly perfumery.

The Sperm whale has no baleen plates for straining out food; but its lower jaw is furnished with forty to fifty immense conical teeth, which fit into grooves or sockets in the untoothed upper jaw. These teeth are nine inches long and one of them will weigh about three pounds. This whale feeds on squids or cuttle fishes, and the teeth are exactly adapted to hold its slippery prey which are soon forced down the ample throat.

There are some other mammals which breathe air and yet are specially adapted for life in the water. We ought not to overlook the seals and the sea lions. Seals are divided into three families: First, the Earless or True Seals; second, the Eared Seals, and third, the Walrus. They have long, fish-like bodies, with fore and hind limbs modified into paddles. We have all noticed the extremely clumsy movements of the seal on land. It shuffles along on its fore-feet, dragging its hind feet. But the spine is very flexible and so the body is urged forward by a series of awkward jerks and twistings of the spinal column. This spine, with its attached muscles, is the Seal's chief motor power in swimming, so that in the water it is as rapid and graceful as it is ungainly on land. They live, of course, mainly on fish, so can exist only by proving swifter than their prey.

All Seals have hairy coats, rendered waterproof by a fatty secretion from the skin. Usually, a thick layer of fat beneath the skin protects them from the cold. Most of them prefer the cold waters of the northern latitudes.

There are about eighteen species of Earless Seals, all frequenting the temperate and colder waters; all of them without external ears. They can remain under water for a long time—from five to fifteen minutes. At every breath the nostrils open wide and close again by means of a constricting muscle, called a sphincter; thus when the creature is submerged no water can pass into the lungs.

They assemble in small herds. Each Seal consumes about seven pounds of fish per day. This Seal is easily tamed and becomes strongly attached to its human friends. The Greenland Seals assemble in immense herds, and of these, the annual catch is very heavy.

The matrimonial alliances of the Elephant Seals, the largest of the family, are conducted on the principle that the strongest males take the best females, the weaker males taking those females that are left, if any. During the season of courtship, the males fight desperately, inflicting fearful wounds with their tusk-like teeth, with which they can crack stones as if they were nutshells. Each victorious combatant selects a considerable number of wives over whom he rules with despotic sway. He is very careful of their safety and will defend them with his life, if necessary.

The Sea Lion is simply a huge hair Seal, ten feet long, eight or ten feet in circumference, and weighing as much as 1,200 pounds. They are very noisy, keeping up a constant uproar, the old animals bellowing like bulls, and the younger ones bleating like sheep.

The Walrus or Sea Horse is a monster of the deep in a class all its own. It has a strange head with projecting muzzle bristling with long wiry hairs, and a couple of enormous canine teeth that project from the upper jaw. These tusks grow until they are two feet long and weigh from four to nine pounds. They are useful for raking up molluscs out of the mud and form excellent grappling hooks to climb out of the water on to the ice.

The Walrus is a valuable animal, its skin, teeth and oil being in demand. It is practically confined to the Arctic regions where, when they were more numerous than now, hunters have obtained as much as 30,000 pounds of ivory in a single year. It has been calculated that in ten years more than 100,000 of them have been destroyed to furnish two million gallons of oil and 400,000 pounds of ivory.

Here again is the infinite wisdom of God. He brought the waters into being, designing this fluid for the home of various sorts of animals and fishes and then proceeded to prepare the creatures for the waters. We have been impressed again and again with the infinite variety of the Creator's plans. Whenever a special organ is needed, it is always forthcoming. No matter how difficult the environment, the animals which have been placed there find themselves in possession of the precise faculties, instincts, and organs which enable them to survive.

Man has been allotted the surface of the earth for his home. We are surrounded with all sorts of strange and often menacing conditions. The greatest of these dangers is an invisible personal Devil operating against humanity. He has challenged God for world-control and is ambitious for power and for worship. In the unseen realms there is going on a tremendous conflict which rages around men and women, few of whom are conscious of the ceaseless struggle between two mighty Powers.

God has told us the story in His Book, and has repeatedly given us warnings, offering us a sure way of escape from the Devil's attack. Sad to say, this divine warning is largely ignored, but there are some who listen and obey. They will escape the judgment of those who do not come into line with God's demands.

Where are you—and you—and you? As one of God's ambassadors, I have been commissioned to give you this message, and to extend to you this urgent invitation to link up with Jesus Christ. What is your answer?

CHAPTER XXIV

HIPPO, GIRAFFE, AND MOUNTAIN GOAT

Some other strange and interesting mammals deserve our attention in this study we are making, so today let us look at the Hippopotamus or River Horse, next to the elephant in bulk among the quadrupeds. It frequents the rivers and lakes of different regions of Africa. Owing to its short legs, it is not more than four or five feet high at the shoulders, but its length varies from twelve to fourteen feet. A full-grown animal with its swollen, barrel-like body may weigh four tons.

It has a rough, tough, warty hide, slaty copperbrown in color, the female being of a lighter shade. The skin is practically bare with the exception of a few strong bristles on face, muzzle, neck and tail. This hide, when freshly removed, may weigh five hundred pounds, and as it is one and a half inches thick on the back, is not easily removed. This animal has an enormous head, which is remarkable in shape, with small, erect ears, bulging eyes, and nostrils set in direct line. This feature enables the animal to raise its eyes and nostrils above the water when it wishes to breathe and survey its surroundings without exposing its huge body.

Inside the mouth there is a terrifying armory of gleaming white teeth. How would you enjoy a set like this? The canines curve backwards and may be forty inches long with the average about thirty. The lower incisors lie almost horizontally with their points projecting backwards.

With this equipment the hippopotamus can cut grass and reeds as with shears, or tear up the water plants on which it feeds. When wounded or irritated, it becomes a fearsome enemy, and can crack the sides of a canoe as though it were cardboard. It has been known to cut a man in two with a single snap.

The Hippo loves company and so they collect in herds of twenty or thirty. In some regions hundreds of them may be seen stretching along a few miles of river. It is always difficult to count them as they are continually diving and rising, though they are careful never all to appear above the surface at the same time. It is a good diver, with the ability to close ears and nostrils at will by using special muscles, and can remain below the surface for at least five minutes. A young baby hippopotamus is carried on the neck of the mother which comes to the surface frequently rather than run any risk of drowning her offspring.

Possessed of an enormous appetite which is seldom satisfied, and with a stomach capacity of five or six bushels, it is not difficult to imagine the damage that can be done to standing crops when these animals are on the rampage. Although so huge a creature, it is relatively harmless, thriving and even breeding in captivity.

It is thought that the hippopotamus is "behemoth," and "chief of the ways of God," mentioned in Job, 40th chapter, where we read:

"Lo! now his strength is in his loins,
And his force in the muscles of his belly.
He moveth his tail like a cedar;
The sinews of his thighs are knit together;
His bones are as tubes of brass;

His limbs are like bars of iron.
He is the chief of the ways of God."

The next animal we select for observation from among the mammals is the Giraffe, of which there are ten varieties but only two species, one a southern one and the other northern, the first, in a district running through British East Africa to the Sudan, the second, in the region between Abyssinia and the Nile.

The southern animal has short, close hair, creamy-fawn in color, and marked irregularly with patches of darker fawn and brownish black, with the general resemblance to the coat of a leopard. Upon the top of the head are two horn-like projections, which are merely outgrowth from certain bones of the skull, but are covered with skin and tufted with dark hair.

The Nubian or northern species is more reddish chestnut in color, the skin showing a series of almost geometrical tawny lines, while frequently there is a third horn in the center of the forehead.

The giraffe appears to be a graceful mixture of the antelope, deer, ox, camel, and ostrich. We can understand why it is sometimes known as the camelopard, but its full, round, dark, expressive eyes show that it has nothing in common with fierce flesh-eating animals.

It is the tallest of all living animals, a full-grown male reaching a height of eighteen or twenty feet, the female being slightly shorter. A large part of this great stature is obtained by the extraordinarily long neck, which, however, has only seven vertebrae, as found in all other mammals.

The long tapering neck is not very flexible and so the giraffe presents rather a ludicrous sight when it stoops to drink or graze, being compelled to separate its legs in an awkward straddle in order to reach the ground.

Its great height makes it easy for it to browse upon the leaves of trees, especially the acacia which is its favorite, and causes the skin to give off a powerful odor, not unlike the perfume from a hive of heather honey. The upper lip is very flexible, and the long tongue has such agility and power that the animal is able to pluck with speed and accuracy selected leaves, one at a time.

The giraffe is gentle and inoffensive, but when attacked, will defend itself with a series of vigorous kicks, sometimes effective even against a lion. At all times it is strangely silent, and its voice is unknown. In its sport or play, it utters no sound, not even when startled. Not even does it give vent to a moan of pain when it is in the agonies of death, clasped by a lion, which usually stalks its prey unobserved and bears it to the ground by sheer strength.

Like some of the antelopes and the camels, it can go a long time without water, obtaining sufficient moisture from its food. They thrive well in captivity.

Do you know about the mountain goat which lives high on the mountains during the winter, where no other mammal stays? There in that dangerous region the mother goat must teach her offspring how to jump from crag to crag. The lesson is a severe one. When they come to the end of the trail or to the edge of a ledge, which is a dangerous spot selected by the mother, naturally the little fellow hesitates, so mother promptly pushes it over the cliff. Very terrified, the young goat manages to strike his feet against a jutting rock, and bounces to another trail far below.

This all may happen some 9,000 feet or more above sea level. The ledges over which baby is pushed may be 1,000 feet high. Mother knows, however, that there is a trail below, and jutting rocks; for she has made these jumps, herself, many times before. The feet of the mountain goat are made "non-skid." There is a sharp-horned hoof, and inside, a pad which permits the feet to stick to slippery rocks.

Yes, the mountain goat teaches its young how to walk in slippery places. But the Christian has a much better Guide and Protector. Remember Psalm 91:10-12:

> "There shall no evil befall thee . . . for He
> will give His angels charge over thee, to
> keep thee in all thy ways. They shall bear
> thee up in their hands, lest thou dash thy
> foot against a stone."

And listen to Psalm 94:18:

> "When I said, my foot slippeth; Thy loving
> kindness, O Lord, held me up."

And Psalm 17:5:

> "My steps have held fast to Thy paths, my
> feet have not slipped." "Thy right hand
> hath holden me up." (Ps. 18:35.)

Today we walk in a world which is dark and the road we travel is full of pitfalls and hidden dangers. Without the "Light of the world," to illumine our pathway, and the strong, helping hand of the Son of God, we shall surely stumble and fall. Are you walking with steady steps—unafraid and confident? If you know not

Christ, I can answer this question for you. I know that you are having many disastrous falls. The way to safe travel along life's highway is given in some lines of Arthur Lynn:

"You ask me why a life serene is mine,
And why I take no thought for things of
    time.
The answer, Friend, will make the secret
    thine.
GOD WALKS WITH ME.

You daily trudge along the winding way
And find no comfort at the close of day,
Whilst I, o'er things terrestrial, hold my
    sway—
GOD WALKS WITH ME.

And so, my friend, in this strange world
    of doubt,
Just put those inbred enemies to rout.
Then you can give the exultant shout—
GOD WALKS WITH ME!"

Yes, if God walks with you, nothing can harm you. He is always on hand to guard and protect.

"Jesus, my Lord, is a wall about me.
Dwelling in Him, I can dwell secure.
Nothing can harm me for naught can reach
    me
Save what He willeth that I endure.

Jesus, my Lord, is my Shield and Buckler.
Unto all evil the way is barred.

Nothing can harm me, for naught can find
    me
Save what He willeth shall cross His guard.

Jesus, my Lord, is my lofty Tower;
Where He hath set me in peace on high.
Nothing can harm me, for naught can find
    me,
Save what He willeth shall pass Him by."

(Annie Johnson Flint)

I would like to add my humble witness. Jesus Christ to me is such a wonderful Saviour. I have proved Him times without number. He never fails.

You have nothing to lose except your sins and your judgment by taking Him. Such a decision is all profit and no loss. What about it?

CHAPTER XXV

THE STRANGE STORY OF BABY KANGAROO

We turn today to another class of animals known as the Marsupials or pouched animals, all of them, with one exception, inhabitants of Australia and a few adjacent islands. Many of the species show considerable differences from one another in external appearance, and not a few would pass as members of other orders of mammals.

All of them, however, are distinguished by the presence of a pouch or bag in the lower part of the abdomen. The Latin word, marsupium, which gives them their name, means a pouch or bag. In this bag are very tiny nipples connected with the milk-producing glands of the mother. For our purpose it will be sufficient to confine our study to an extraordinary member of this group of animals—the kangaroo, perhaps giving a moment's attention to the opossum, the only one not native to Australia.

Kangaroos range in size from animals standing five feet and over, to forms no larger than rats, but all showing a remarkable similarity of build. They are vegetarians exclusively and rely for safety upon speed for which purpose the hind legs are immensely exaggerated. The tail is developed to form a counterpoise when traveling in a semi-erect posture, and also to act as a support when seated. If cornered, a kangaroo can rest on the tail alone and strike out with both hind feet at the same time. The small fore limbs are efficient grasping organs.

The hind legs are about three and a half feet long, ending in strong feet with four toes, each powerfully clawed. The fourth toe is developed into a long solid nail, nearly twelve inches in length, and forming a formidable offensive weapon. The tail measures three feet in length.

The front teeth of the kangaroo are remarkable in that there are from two to six in the upper jaw, but only two in the lower. These have knife-like edges, and, being movable, serve as a pair of shears for clipping the grass on which the animals feed.

When the animal sits supported on its hind feet and tail, it is rather more than four feet high, but when standing erect, is almost as tall as a full-grown man. The female is so much smaller that she might be taken for an entirely different species.

The color of the rather woolly fur is brown, mingled with grey, but the fore-feet and the tip of the tail are black. The eyes are large, round, soft, and beautiful, giving it a gentle expression that compensates for the rather savage appearance of the teeth gleaming white between the cleft lips.

The kangaroo moves awkwardly on all fours when grazing or walking short distances. When alarmed, it travels by a series of hops, each leap measuring about fifteen feet. By this method of progression, utilizing to the full the powerful hind legs, it shows enormous speed, and in full flight can clear bushes or fences nine feet high.

The truly astonishing features of this animal concern the pouch, and the way the young are born, and find the difficult passage to the pouch, where they are reared by the mother. There is only one young kangaroo at a birth and this comes into existence in a very immature form. When it leaves its mother's uro-genital sinus, it is barely an inch long, soft, naked, blind, helpless, and semi-transparent as an earthworm. It is born thirty-nine days after its ante-natal life began.

It has been given a strange instinct which causes it, immediately after it is born in the open, to try to find its way into mother's pouch. Accordingly it makes its way on knees and elbows up the legs to the maternal abdomen, fighting its way along a tract of hair, licked smooth by the mother until it finds the pouch. Entering the pouch, it searches blindly in the darkness for one of the two nipples therein. Finding it, this is grasped in the mouth, the teat swelling into a bulb filling the infant's mouth cavity. At the same time a circular muscle surrounding the lips of the baby kangaroo contracts in a tight involuntary spasm, which holds it firmly attached to this part of the mother.

The reason for this is that it has at this stage no power to suck, and although so close to nourishment, would die if the feeding process were not automatic. The mother is possessed of a real pumping apparatus in the form of a contractile, mammary gland muscle under control of her will. When baby is safely attached to the nipple and ready for its first meal, the milk is pumped directly into the mouth of the waiting baby, which, in Australia, always goes by the name of "Joey."

And now there is another very curious and interesting feature which could not possibly be a chance arrangement. Here is a semi-conscious, immature baby without power to suck, having fluid pumped into its mouth and throat. At once we ask why it does not choke as it undoubtedly would do without the strange device seen in the structure of the windpipe. Without this change death would surely be the lot of this tiny kangaroo. In order to prevent choking, the windpipe, which in other mammals, and in humans, terminates at the same level as the gullet, is elongated and shunted forward into the back opening of the nasal chamber. Thus air gets right down to the lungs, but no milk goes the wrong way.

It is very interesting to find a similar adaptation in a whalebone whale, in which, as it rushes through the water with mouth wide open, the glottis or windpipe is pushed forward into the back opening of the nasal chamber. At the same time the front nostrils, "blow-holes" (anterior nares) are closed by valves, and so no water gets down to the lungs of the whale.

To attribute this phenomenon to Nature or chance is to put an impossible strain on our credulity. Here is design of the most pronounced character.

In this internal cradle the young kangaroo passes its earlier stages of development and does not generally face the open until about six months old. Before this age, of course, it does leave its mother's protecting pouch, never going very far afield, however, as it nibbles the grass. At the first sign of danger it rushes for the perambulator pocket which is always ready to receive it. It leaps head first into this safe haven, and then turns around to peep out on the world.

The opossums are small tree-dwelling mammals feeding principally upon a mixed diet of vegetable food, birds, eggs, insects and the smallest animals avail-

able. The Virginia opossum is a native of the southern
states, about three feet long, with a twelve-inch tail,
and is about the size of a large cat. Its nest is built in
some hollow tree, fallen or standing, or under the protection of old projecting roots.

A dozen or more young opossums are born at a
time, less than an inch long, each weighing about four
grains. At the end of only a week of feeding in the
pouch they will weigh as much as thirty grains. When
five weeks old, they climb to the mother's back, clinging to her fur with their claws, twisting their tails
around mother's conveniently placed and large terminal
extremity.

The opossum is cunning, and when captured, immediately simulates death with jaws open, tongue extended, eyes dimmed. Even if kicked and beaten, it will
not quiver a muscle or flicker an eyelid, but if the
gaze of its tormentor be removed for but an instant,
away scampers the apparently dead animal.

It will be seen that these animals possess powers
which are denied humans. They have that mysterious
"instinct" which no one understands. On this power,
the life of the individual depends, and likewise the
propagation of the species. This instinct cannot be
learned; the animal has it immediately when it is
born. Without it, death would be its certain lot. It
could not have been evolved, because it must be in a
perfect condition from the very beginning in order
that the various forms of life may continue their existence. There is but one satisfactory explanation—creation by a wise God.

Notice the place of safety for these animal children
—close to the heart of the parent. How like the only

secure Refuge for us. When danger threatens us, when the storms beat upon us, and disaster comes close, there is always a Rock which provides a quiet resting place.

Listen to the comforting words that our Heavenly Father speaks to us:

> "The name of the Lord is a strong tower; the righteous runneth into it and is safe." (Prov. 18:10.)

> "God is our refuge and strength, a very present help in trouble. Therefore will we not fear . . . the Lord of hosts is with us; the God of Jacob is our refuge . . . Be still and know that I am God. (Ps. 46.)

> "My soul, wait thou in silence for God only; for my expectation is from Him. He only is my rock and my salvation; He is my high tower; I shall not be moved . . . Trust in Him at all times . . . God hath spoken." (Ps. 62.)

> "The high hills are a refuge for the wild goats; the rocks are a refuge for the conies . . . I cry unto the Lord with my voice . . . I said, Thou art my refuge, my portion in the land of the living . . . in Thee do I trust; cause me to know the way wherein I should walk . . . I flee unto Thee to hide me." (Psalms 104 and 142.)

> "O Lord, how manifold are Thy works! In wisdom hast Thou made them all. The earth is full of Thy riches . . . I will sing unto the Lord as long as I live; I will sing

praise to my God while I have any being."
(Ps. 104.)

Today when the foundations of civilization are
crashing around us, what a confidence is ours when we
remember that "the foundation of God standeth sure,
having this seal, the Lord knoweth them that are His."
(2 Tim. 2:19.)

It looks as if we are now in this period. The Lord
said: "Men's hearts failing them for fear and for looking after those things that are coming on the earth."
Our Lord spoke of some conditions that would mark
the end of the age, prior to His return to earth.

Can you afford to take any chance in regard to your
foundation? The greatest storm that has ever dev-
astated the earth will shortly bring world destruction;
and even now is brewing. Have you any safe shelter?

There is one sure Refuge—the Lord Jesus Christ.
Will you enter today?

CHAPTER XXVI

NATURE'S RADAR EXPERT

Today we examine some incomparably quaint creatures, members of the mammal family. They are "bats," usually regarded with superstitious dread, and viewed with repugnance by many people. They belong to the Order, Chiroptera, this word derives from two Greek words, meaning "hand" and "wing." As the word indicates, then, they are "hand-winged" animals.

The early naturalists were much puzzled when they tried to classify them. Some called them birds because they could fly; others, quadrupeds because they could walk; and when eventually they were viewed as mammals, they were placed at the end of the list as a sort of connecting link between fur and feathers.

They are mammals through and through, covered with hair, and giving milk to their young, and yet they are aerial as most birds. The bat has four limbs and a tail, the fingers of the front limbs being remarkably elongated, to serve as supports for a thin, semi-transparent membrane, which is a prolongation of the skin of the flanks. The arms are incapable of rotary movement, but the skin-enshrined fingers are able to beat the air rapidly with the steady strokes necessary for flight.

The short thumb is armed with a strong projecting hook-like claw, by which the bat can attach itself to any convenient object, as well as help itself along a level surface.

They are found in practically all parts of the world and vary in size from that of a small mouse to a creature with a wing-span of several feet. Their facial appearance is exceedingly grotesque because of the peculiar development of muzzle and ears. The former is known as a nose-leaf, while in some, the ears are membranously expanded into such lengths that they can be folded as though they were wings. Imagine a mule with such appendages!

There are more than 400 species, the great majority, insect eaters, although a few add a little fruit to their diet, and Vampire bats love to suck blood. The ear and nose of the bat are always highly developed organs of extreme delicacy, and seem to account for the animal's almost supernatural sense of touch.

The peculiar wing membrane which I mentioned a moment ago, is a kind of silky skin that begins at the side of the neck, passes along the front surface of the arm, skips the clawed thumb, and is stretched out on four very long fingers. From the back surface of the arm, the membrane reaches along the sides of the body and is continued down the leg as far as the ankle. Another membrane arises from the ankle, and extends between the hind legs, including the tail, if one is present.

This wing-membrane has drawn the leg outwards in a strange manner and the knee points, not forwards, but backwards.

A bat cannot stand up, and although it can alight on its resting place head upwards, and may remain fixed by its thumbs, the common position when at rest is head downwards, clinging by the well-clawed toes of one or both feet. A bat resting quietly on all fours has the knees turned upwards, and the elbows touching the knees—a quaint posture.

Bats can launch themselves into the air even from off the ground, and their flight is masterly. Contrary to a widely-held idea, bats have eyes which are small and poorly developed, not providing them with any considerable degree of sight. Yet, they are able to fly with amazing speed and cleverness, avoiding all kinds of obstacles in a room, diving under a couch, constantly looping the loop, indulging in sudden somersaults, and outdoors in rapid and noiseless motion capturing moths, gnats, and flying-bettles with unerring skill.

This animal can thread its way amid boughs of trees with a facility quite beyond its powers of sight, and does it with the greatest of ease even when the darkness is profound. In fact, it always seems to prefer darkness to light.

This curious power led to an interesting experiment, which has been repeated many times by curious investigators, to ascertain how the bat avoids collision with any impediments placed in its path, no matter how small or large or numerous.

The bats' eyes were temporarily sealed up, so as to render them quite blind, and then the bats were liberated in a chamber in which were suspended cloths with holes little bigger than the bat's body. Strings were stretched at short intervals all through the room in order to increase the difficulties.

Though deprived of sight, they flitted about without the least embarrassment, passing unerringly through the holes in the cloths, missing the strings with their flapping wings, turning corners at break-neck speed, and seeming to enjoy their phenomenal performance, even to finding crannies for concealment, when the fun was over.

The closing of the bats' ears seems to cause rather more difficulty, but even then their tortuous flight among the various obstructions was not greatly hindered. It is evident that in its nocturnal evolutions the bat is guided by some unknown power, scarcely less than a sixth sense, of which humans know nothing, and which probably lies in the exquisite nervous system of the wings. In fact, this seems to be a perfected form of radar.

With few exceptions bats love company and their number runs into the thousands and possibly millions under favorable circumstances. Probably the most remarkable bat cave in the world is in Texas, from which at night for two hours at a stretch a rapidly moving stream of bats will emerge—a veritable cloud of flying forms.

The bats of northern countries, in the winter time, pass into a state of true hibernation, sinking into a complete coma, their breathing movements scarcely perceptible, and the heart beating about twenty-five times a minute. For their winter sleep they prefer a hollow tree, a corner of the church tower, an opening under the thatch of barns, or a crevice in a cave.

Ordinary bats give birth to one baby bat, occasionally two. One baby is about all a mother bat can manage. During nursing time (June until August) the young bat clings with its toes and thumbs to its mother's hair, its mouth to its mother's breast, the parent flitting and wheeling, glancing and doubling in rapid flight—business as usual! When the mother rests, she folds her wings around her child. The females live together in colonies apart from the males, until late autumn, when both sexes decide to be sociable—the time of pairing. There is an extraordinary fact here. Although pairing is in the autumn, the internal fertilization of the egg-cells does not occur until the following spring. One writer, commenting on this unusual feature, says: "Thus the disadvantage of having the young ones developing during the starvation hibernating period is avoided, and the carrying of the young before birth is reduced to a minimum. And then, this writer adds, "NATURE'S WAYS ARE WONDROUS WISE."

There is no doubt that in the many astonishing features which have been described today there is evidence of marvelous wisdom. Man's explanation is that "Nature's ways are wondrous wise." However, this is not a satisfactory solution, unless we substitute the words "God, the Creator" for Nature. Then it makes sense.

I find in Paley's "Natural Theology," written sixty years ago, these words in an argument which still is unanswerable. He writes:

"Design, if established, proves the Personality of the Deity, as distinguished from what is sometimes called Nature, or a principle . . . That which can contrive, or design, must be a person. The seat of intelligence is a Person."

Now this is the argument I have been driving home in almost every talk, as you know. It is the only possible view to take, if we admit the inevitable logic of all the great mass of evidence uncovered before us. There is nothing of credulity in this idea. It cannot be called a figment of childish imagination. It is a wholly sane and intelligent conclusion. It is simply the result of applying the test given by God, Himself, in Romans 1:20:

> "The invisible things of Him from the creation of the world are clearly seen, being understood by the things that are made, even His eternal power and Godhead; so that they are without excuse."

These are strong words. They must be heard and obeyed. The end of those who preferred to eject God from their consciousness was that "GOD GAVE THEM UP." This would be the most terrible judgment ever imagined—an eternal separation from God.

God gave to the bat many remarkable powers, after denying this life-form many of the capacities of other animals. At least they do not seem to be equipped to carry on without great difficulty; and yet, the first bat that appeared on the scene used the strange equipment with which it came into existence, and all the millions of descendents have been using them ever since.

Even parental love is given this unusual animal. The mother wraps herself around her helpless babe, and it is safe to say that this child experiences no fear when the strong hands enfold it.

How like our safety in Christ. He tells us in John 10:28, 29:

> "I give unto them eternal life, and they shall never perish, and no one shall snatch them out of My hand.

> "My Father who gave them to Me is greater

than all; and no one is able to snatch them
out of My Father's hand."

May I ask you again, if you are conscious of this
safety? As civilization crashes, the omnipotent hand
of our Lord is the only Refuge which gives us security.
Will you, if you have not already done so, make sure
of heaven? There's no other name given among men,
whereby we may be saved but the name of Jesus
Christ. With that name on our lips and in our hearts,
we have immediate access to God and may call Him
Father. Until we link up with Jesus, God is nothing
more than Creator. What is He to you today?

CHAPTER XXVII

ONE OF NATURE'S CARPENTERS

There are many animals which exhibit an astonishing mechanical skill. They are real artisans performing operations which at first glance would seem to indicate a reasoning intelligence, but which on closer examination must be explained as due to the possession of remarkable instincts which we have been discussing in several of these talks.

Today we look at the beaver—one of the gnawing mammals or rodents. Squirrels are near relatives, although not adapted for life in the water as are the beavers.

At one time the beaver was to be found throughout the forest regions of the entire northern part of the Northern Hemisphere. It ranged over the whole of Europe, and was an inhabitant of the British Isles until about the beginning of the 11th century. Now, however, the European beaver is nearly extinct, and a similar fate presses hard upon its American brother. Its gradual disappearance is due, of course, to the value of its beautiful coat of fur, which has led to wholesale slaughter.

The color of the long shining hair which covers the back of the animal is a chestnut brown, and the fine wool that lies next to the skin is a soft grayish brown. The animal is long and slender, of a total length of about three feet and a half, with a twelve-inch tail, flat, paddle-shaped and scale-covered. The legs are short and strong, and the hind feet are webbed, thus adapting it for swimming. The flat tail makes an excellent rudder. It used to be thought that the beaver used this tail as a trowel, to apply mud to the outer surface of the dams and lodges, but there is no reason to believe this to be true. As a matter of fact, exaggeration is not necessary in describing the accomplishments of this capable builder. The simple truth is amazing enough.

Safety from their enemies is provided by their ability to swim and dive and to remain under water for as long as fifteen minutes; also, their nocturnal habits and their wide range of diet make for prolonged life. They can eat many different kinds of vegetable food, and show great cleverness in secreting twigs and branches, for the sake of the bark which is one of their chief articles of diet. They live a communal life, and display an anxiety to help one another, with an inborn efficiency which merits our admiration.

Their favorite home is beside some small stream which has its course through well-wooded country. They prefer willows, birches, maples and poplars, because they like the bark of these trees. They know how to fell trees, often, up to sixteen inches in diameter. With the chisel-edged front teeth the beaver cuts two parallel furrows across the grain of the wood, and then wrenches off the part between, in a succession of chips. Next, it makes other parallel lines, and gouges off another circle of chips. It goes on doing this until an hour-glass excavation has been made around the tree, which then falls.

The tree usually falls directly across the stream, and those who have written in too glowing terms about the skill exhibited have told us that the beaver calculates carefully just how to cut through the tree so that it falls exactly in the right place. This is perhaps attributing too great powers to it, as frequently the tree falls the wrong way. The fact remains though, that in most cases the branches are in the water just where they are needed to construct their lodges and the dam, and where the smaller branches and twigs are easily accessible for food.

The purpose of the building of the dam is to bring about a depth of water sufficient to erect a series of lodges or houses in which they can live in safety from enemies, and in which they can store their food.

These dams are remarkable structures, often of great length—frequently more than one hundred and fifty yards. They run across the stream from bank to bank, either in a straight line or if the stream is rapid and deep, requiring additional strength in the dam, they build it with the convexity facing the stream—an admirable feature of their planning.

By means of these dams the beavers are able to convert even small rivulets into large pools of water, using the felled tree, which is cut up into lengths of from five to six feet. They fill in the gaps with smaller sticks, roots, grasses and moss, all plastered with mud and clay in a most workman like manner until the whole structure is made perfectly water-tight.

The lodge is a dome-shaped structure, composed of sticks, grass and moss, all woven together and plastered with mud, increasing in size and in the thickness of the walls, year by year, as fresh material is added for repairs. Within this dome-shaped house is a central chamber with its floor a little above the level of the water and with two shafts which have their outer apertures beneath the water.

One of these shafts is driven at a straight and moderate incline. It is up this that the beavers drag the pieces of wood and bark to be stored in the lodge to form the winter food supply.

The other shaft is more abrupt in its descent, often winding in its course, and is said to be the usual means of entrance and exit.

The central chamber varies in size, but the larger ones generally measure about seven or eight feet in diameter and two or three feet in height. The floor is snugly carpeted with grass, bark and wood chips. Some beaver lodges are fifteen to twenty feet in diameter and seven or eight feet high but the thickness of the walls leaves, even in the larger structures, a living room of only about seven feet in diameter by three feet in height, accommodating half a dozen animals.

Beavers breed once a year only, bearing three to five at a litter, and the young may live with the parents for years. Most colonies are composed of interrelated family parties, dwelling together in a social and friendly manner, which might well be the envy of humans.

There are many interesting points about the beavers' dam and their houses. Occasionally the branches which have been built into the dam begin to grow and sprout into rooted bushes, thus strengthening the construction and hiding it in green in the summer.

The canals built by these animals excite our admiration. As long as there are suitable trees near their lodges, the beavers have no need of canals, but as the trees are gradually destroyed the animals are forced to go farther and farther afield to secure their food. If the felled trees are beside the water, well and good, for the branches, cut into short sections, can be carried in their mouths as they swim. Their front paws are used like hands to grasp whatever they can hold, as they are not needed in swimming.

When trees at some distance overland are needed, the beavers are compelled to build canals. Their heavy bodies and short legs with webbed hind feet make land travel or the toting of burdens difficult. They must travel under water in order to be safe and secluded.

The best of these canals are very remarkable and may be several hundred feet in length. They may make a short cut between one bend of a snaky stream and another. They may cut right through an island. Making a long tunnel is a task which cannot be accomplished by the individual beaver, but must be tackled cooperatively.

Many lodges, built around a big beaver pond, make a beaver village. The beavers live together in pairs, keeping true to their mates, and exhibit an ordered family life.

Here again we are seeing the operation of the strange and fascinating instinct of animals. The beavers live to provide for themselves and family. They labor to produce and maintain a home. All their efforts are in the direction of living safely and comfortably. They seem to look ahead, and so provide themselves with ample supplies of food, exercising their powers in every direction in order to make a quiet family life possible.

We humans have the same inherent ambition. Fathers and mothers exert every effort to provide comfortable and secure homes for themselves and the members of the family. Our life on earth is largely occupied with this job of getting and holding a home.

The beaver works only for that short period of time during which he occupies the lodge that has been built so laboriously and yet so skillfully, using the dam to provide a sufficient depth of water, so that when danger threatens, they may hasten to their place of refuge, which is partly below water and partly above. To get to their central room, they must pass through a channel of water, which very effectively blocks those animal enemies, for which, naturally, they are no match in a stand-up fight.

We provide for a home during our earth life, but we look for another and different existence in a place of which we know so little. Of one thing we are sure. We shall live on eternally. What kind of home shall we have? Is there any one who can give us information? Has any inhabitant of earth ever visited the unseen realms and returned to give us the facts? To this question there is but one answer and that is in the negative. But God has not left us in the dark. Remember what Jesus said in John 14:2, "In my Father's house are many mansions . . . I go to prepare a place for you." The word "mansions" may be translated, "resting-places," which is a very satisfying thought.

To whom is He speaking? To His disciples, not to the world. And so we are sure that there is a "resting-place" for every man, woman and child on earth, who has joined up with Christ. He builds this place for us. It belongs to the "many mansions" in the capacious "house" of His Father. This is an exciting prospect. We know that there is a competent Carpenter and Builder guaranteeing an eternal home for His followers.

Will you permit me to come a bit closer in this meditation? May I ask you if you experience a feeling of irritation when the name of Jesus Christ is mentioned? Some do. It may be you do not object to the name of God, but, somehow, you wish that I would not keep on referring to the Son of God. The last thing in my mind is to offend my listeners, but I would be guilty if I failed to show you the only way we can be sure of a heavenly home. And there is JUST ONE WAY. And that way is by and through Him Who said He was the Way, the Truth and the Life, the Lord Jesus Christ. Are you "Going My Way"? It leads "HOME."

CHAPTER XXVIII

SOME OBNOXIOUS ANIMALS

Our study today concerns the family of Weasels, rather a large and important one, represented almost everywhere across the globe. Many members of this family are quite snake-like in appearance and, because of their slender, elongated figures, are called the vermiform of worm-like animals. Most of them are burrowers as well as agile climbers, and the leaping power of many is out of all proportion to their short legs.

Although the teeth are not so exclusively flesh-eating as are those of the cats, the canines are long, sharp, and slightly curved backwards; the molars are studded with points and edges. In size these animals do not appear formidable, but no creatures will more quickly pick a fight, are more fierce, or possess more bloodthirsty habits.

They are mainly land animals, preying on small mammals, birds, etc., very often doing nothing more than to suck the blood of their victims. The otters are the aquatic section of the family, and are equally destructive to fish. All these members of the Weasel family bite with unerring instinct into a large artery or vein. It is this deadly form of attack, added to their highly developed muscular system, that enables them to overcome creatures many times their size and actual strength. Most of them are rather obnoxious, especially as to odor, but some of them are clothed with magnificent fur.

The family consists of three sections, viz., the

Weasels proper, the Skunks and Badgers, and the Otters. Together, they include the Pine Marten, the Sable, the Polecat, the Weasel proper, the Stoat or Ermine, the Ferret, the Mink, the Wolverene or Glutton, the Skunk, the Badger and the Otter. We shall not indulge in any minute examination of each of these forms but I draw your attention to a few of them.

The Pine Marten is an inhabitant of the northern regions of both hemispheres, but is becoming scarce in many parts. It is a tree-loving animal, only twenty inches long with a long and bushy tail. The fur is of varying shades of brown and a really fine skin which is only slightly inferior to the celebrated Sable.

The Sable is now almost restricted to eastern Siberia, so persistent has been its slaughter. It has one of the finest furs, of deeper, richer brown than that of the Marten, and is at its peak of perfection during the depth of the northern winter.

The Polecat is slightly smaller than the Marten with a much shorter tail. It is a most noxious pest to the farmyard and no animal is more deadly to rabbits, game, and poultry.

Its inner fur coat is pale yellow in color with an outer covering of dark brown hair, the head being marked with black and white. It has a lust for killing, easily putting to death twenty times more victims than it can eat, and in many cases sucking only the blood and eating the brain. When wounded or irritated, the Polecat emits a foul odor from a pouch near the root of the tail, and this constitutes the distinguishing feature to most people.

The Weasel is one of the smallest of the family, measuring only about ten inches in length, including the tail. The fur is bright reddish on the upper parts, while underneath it is pure white. It is rather pretty, but, for its size, there is no more bloodthirsty creature in the entire animal world. It is exceedingly worm-like in build, and can burrow its way into the runs of rats and mice upon which it wages unceasing war.

It hunts by scent and will even cross water to leap on the back of its victim, burying the teeth in the back of the neck or in the brain. The Weasel is the most prolific of the whole family. Most of them have a litter of four or five young in the spring, but the Weasel proper will have three or four families during the year.

The Ermine, known also as the Stoat, is a vicious little beast, an inverterate slayer of any creature which it can overpower. It is only fourteen inches long, the tail accounting for one-third, but there is considerable variation in size. In an Ermine's larder have been found as many as fifty pheasant eggs removed into hiding with such care that not one shell was cracked; in another case five hares and four rabbits were in storage. The bodies were unmangled except for the single death-wound in the throat or back of the neck. In the higher and colder latitudes the winter coat of the animal is long and quite white—a beautiful and valuable fur.

The Ferret is a whitish or pale yellow animal with pink eyes, and is really only a variety of the Polecat. It is a native of Africa and was introduced into Europe by way of Spain. It is kept in a state of semi-domestication for use in rat-catching and rabbit-hunting. One of my earliest recollections and one of the most exciting is of seeing a half-tamed Ferret, released from the hands of its keeper, attack, with apparent joy, a large rat, much bigger than itself. I shall not forget the courageous skill which brought speedy death to the rat.

The Wolverene or Glutton, though only two or three feet long, in addition to its thick, bushy tail of seven or eight inches, is so stoutly built as to resemble a small bear. It is covered with long hair, mainly brownish in color, the sides being a lighter tint. The muzzle is black, as are the paws, whose ivory-white claws stand out curiously. The Wolverene is the inveterate enemy of the Beaver, the subject of our immediately preceding talk. The Beaver in open battle would be no match for this fierce enemy, but is safe when it reaches the seclusion of the lodge, its dwelling place of security.

The Mink, largely equatic in habit, may best be described as a water polecat, living chiefly on fish, frogs, crayfish, and any small mammals that frequent water. Its body is from fifteen to eighteen inches in length and is more stoutly built than the majority of Weasels.

The fur of the Mink is almost dark chocolate in color and is highly valued. At the present time one first-class Mink pelt will bring as much as $30.00. They have one family a year, usually a litter of four or five. The mother Mink is very particular about exposing any of her newborn children to the gaze of humans while the young are in the suckling stage. If a person forces his way in and takes a look, the indignant parent proceeds to eat all her little ones in a rage of resentment.

The Skunk is an American animal, found in the northern regions of the continent, while the White-backed Skunk ranges over all South and Central America, as far north as Texas. This animal is about a foot and a half in length, exclusive of the long bushy tail. Its legs are short and furnished with sharp claws for burrowing. Like many of their relatives, Skunks have a long bill of fare, from grasshoppers to rats, from wasps to frogs, from fish to ground-nesting birds. While they levy toll on game-birds, they pay man back by checking the number of injurious insects.

The mother Skunk takes great care of her young ones—a half dozen or so, in the comfortable nest that is made in the recess of the burrow or den. The mother provides not only food but education. When she is teaching them the ways of the woods, they often follow her in long Indian file.

The Skunk owes most of its safety to the intolerable smell of the secretion squirted out from two glands near the end of the food-canal. The animals are conspicuous by day in their jet-black fur with two white stripes along the dorsal surface, and yet they move about with deliberation and confidence. They know the potency of their weapon of defense. Long experience has taught them that they are always given right of way by their animal associates. If any creature disputes it, a double jet of this nauseous secretion, carried for two or three feet, soon brings a disastrous awakening to the rash challenger. These scent sacs may be removed by a simple surgical operation, and as Skunks are rather gentle creatures, they make agreeable household pets—post-operatively, of course! They seem to enjoy man's company and protection, and their young ones are playful and affectionate.

The Badger is another member of the Weasel tribe and is a marvelous digger, very powerful muscles working the fore-limbs, which are furnished with long curved claws. Its average length is two feet six inches, and its height at the shoulder about one foot. The body is reddish gray in color, changing to whitish-gray on ribs and tail. The head is white, except for a definitely marked black line on each side. The throat, chest, abdomen, legs and feet are of deepest brown.

The food of the Badger consists chiefly of roots, fruits, snails, worms, wild honey, and sometimes young rabbits. Owing to the looseness of its skin, and the thickness of its hair, it can rob the nests of bees and wasps with safety, the stings of the angry insects taking little or no effect.

Naturally a harmless animal, the Badger is a terrible antagonist when provoked. Its sharp teeth can inflict a serious wound, and the jaws lock together by a peculiar contrivance at their junction with the skull, enabling it to retain its death-grip without any special effort.

The Common Otter is rather a fierce, shy animal, largely nocturnal, and living in burrows in a river bank or under the roots of an old tree. It is less than three feet and a half long, including a fourteen inch tail and weighs about twenty-four pounds. It is lithe and serpentine in shape with webbed toes and a long, broad and flat tail, which forms an excellent rudder in the water. It is really a water-weasel, and like most of this family, very rapacious, and always bent on destruction.

We have looked today at a group of animals whose habits, for the most part, do not appeal to us, I am sure. They combine good and bad features, but all of them show the same instinctive powers suited to their special manner of life.

When God created all these various forms, it must have been very interesting, even to Him whose creative power is infinite. All things have been created for His glory. The same purpose of God is revealed when we look at ourselves. Man, created perfect at first, chose to defy and disobey his Creator. Ever since, man has persisted in the exercise of his will against the will of God, with the result that today the world of humanity is on the verge of the abyss, torn apart by the ravages of war.

We are confronted by a tremendous scene—warring nations refusing allegiance to God, turning a deaf ear to all His warnings, not only ignoring Him and defying Him, but ridiculing Him. Is there any reason for surprise if dire judgment falls?

Have you interested yourself in God's plan for your life? I have found His plan for me, and in so far as I am able, I do want to work it out for His glory. Take a quiet moment to ask yourself this question: "Am I right with God?" Christ is a WONDERFUL SAVIOUR! Will you take Him?

CHAPTER XXIX

THE KING OF BEASTS

Today we think of another group in the Animal Kingdom—the Order Carnivora, or the Flesh Eaters, among which we are especially interested in the family of Cats, where we find the Lion, "King of Beasts," as he has been called.

This is a large and widely distributed order, composed of many species which feed chiefly, but in a few cases, not exclusively upon flesh. They are the beasts of prey, having special qualifications because of their general conformation and the structure of teeth and claws, which enable them to capture living animals, and to tear and devour the flesh. So dependent are many of these animals upon flesh that not only does a lack of sufficient supply rouse their fiercest passions, but for some of them, complete abstinence means death.

The Cats are at the head of the Carnivora, and in their bodily form are most exquisitely adapted to carry out their implanted instincts. They are powerful in frame, without an atom of superfluous flesh; bone, muscle and sinew all are adapted for general agility, along with free and graceful motion.

The slender limbs are well-knit and supple, and the under surfaces of the feet are padded with elastic cushions to render their footfall noiseless when stealing on their prey. They have very strong, sharply-pointed and curved claws, which can be drawn in when at rest or when the animal walks, so that the weight of the body rests only on the pads. When the creature becomes excited, and thrusts out its paw to strike a blow, or to clutch its prey, the lower tendons tighten, the upper tendons relax, so that the claw is thrown boldly forward, sharp, and instantly ready for use.

Cats walk on their toes, this being an aid to swiftness, but the sharp retractile claws never come into contact with the ground, so are never dulled and blunted. Their heel bones project behind, giving leverage to the limbs for leaping and bounding, thus enabling them to make tremendous and sudden speed to overtake animals that need time to get into full flight.

Their teeth are very distinctive. The incisors have sharp cutting edges, the molars are more or less pointed, and the canines are long, strong, and curved. The jaws are not able to grind, but they are very terrible shears. The wriggling prey is literally skewered, its flesh torn up and bolted in great snatches. The tongue has rough horny projections directed backwards, serving as a rasp to remove the last particles of flesh from the bones. You may have noticed the cleanness of the bones in the cages at the circus after the meal has been finished. Their eyes are adapted for vision by day or night. Their sight is keen, their sense of hearing very acute, and the power of smell remarkably developed, while the long whiskers possess an exquisite sense of feeling.

The skin of the Cat tribe is loosely attached, rendering it difficult for even sharp teeth to get a grip. These features are common to all the Cats. They are elegant in form and often possess a beautiful coloring, but are filled with a crafty suspicion and bloodthirstiness which marks their daily life.

The best known variety of Lion is the South and East African, tawny yellow in color, lighter on the under parts of the body, darker above. The ears are blackish, and the tip of the tail is decorated with a tuft of black hair. No other member of the Cat tribe has a tufted tail.

When fully grown, the male Lion will measure nearly four feet high at the shoulder, eleven feet in length, and may attain a weight of five hundred pounds. It has terrific strength and no animal, except the rhinoceros and the elephant, can resist its power.

The thick, shaggy mane of long hair, which falls from the neck, shoulders and part of the throat and chin, gives the full-grown Lion that regal appearance which endows him with the name—"King of Beasts."

The lioness is smaller than her mate, and lacks the mane which is the distinctive feature of the male. However, it is true that very many of the males have only the semblance of a mane.

Like all the members of the Cat tribe, the Lion is more or less indolent by nature until aroused by the call of hunger. Even then it will not take more trouble than is necessary to supply itself with a satisfying meal.

The Lion launches itself at its prey in a terribly swift bound, endeavoring to accomplish one of two things, either to tear the jugular vein open at the throat, or inflict a deep bite at the back of the neck behind the ears. Quite often, as it alights on the shoulders of its victim, it breaks the latter's neck by a sudden, powerful wrenching of the head with one of its forepaws. Next, with one stroke of its paw, and extended claws, the entrals are torn out, and such delicacies as the heart and liver devoured first; then huge lumps of flesh are gulped down.

The roar of the Lion inspires every other animal with terror, and this aids in securing food for the Lion. If it has been unsuccessful in its night wanderings, this big cat places its mouth close to the earth, and gives vent to terrific roars. The effect is to cause all kinds of creatures to leave their lairs in bewilderment and terror, frantically attempting to escape the threatened danger. This is exactly what the Lion wants, and soon its hunger is appeased by the death of whatever victims it desires to kill.

The Tiger equals the Lion in size, competes with it in strength, and excels it in activity. For elegance of form, grace of movement, and the beauty of its coat, it is much more notable. A full-grown male Tiger may be nine and a half feet long, weighing four hundred and fifty pounds, and some have even attained a length of between thirteen and fourteen feet.

The coat of the Tiger is beautifully marked with contrasting tints. Transverse dark stripes are placed on the bright tawny-yellow groundwork of the body and limbs. Some of these stripes are double, but the majority are single dark streaks. The under parts of the body, chest and throat, and the tufts on each side of the face are almost white; and there the stripes become fainter, fading gradually into the light tint of the fur. The skin is loose, almost to bagginess, and the fur is very thick and close. The brilliant coat of a captive Tiger is very conspicuous; but in its native haunts, it harmonizes completely with the dry, dusky jungle grass; and when crouching along low and scanty vegetation, the big animal may almost be trodden on without being seen. One of the many instances of Nature's camouflage! Its stealthy step is almost inaudible.

As in all members of the Cat family, fierce passions rage in its breast, and its joy is in killing and eating its victim. The cruel yellow fangs, the baleful eyes, the ferocious snarl—all indicate its hatred and fearlessness. In captivity, even after years of training, it cannot be trusted.

The Leopard or Panther is found in Africa from the Mediterranean to Capetown, and everywhere in Southern Asia. With its crafty brain, agile body, sharp teeth and claws, it bears the worst of reputations. Although the Leopard is smaller than the Lion and Tiger, it is to be feared none-the-less. When it is wounded it does not slink off, but will come straight at its foe—a whirlwind of claws, fierce anger, and deadly power.

Among the smaller Cats are two which seem to warrant brief mention in this talk. They are the Ocelot and the Cheetah. The Ocelot is plentiful in the tropical regions of South Africa, about four feet long, with an average height of eighteen inches. The light greyish-fawn fur is richly marked with broken bands of deeper fawn edged with black. The ears are black except for a conspicuous white spot behind and near the base of the ear. Its skin is used in making various articles of dress.

The Cheetah or Hunting Leopard is an elegantly formed and beautifully marked creature, inhabiting southwestern Asia and many parts of India, and east and south Africa. It much resembles a long and slender-limbed leopard with a head small in proportion to its height. It is three feet high at the shoulder with a length of five feet, exclusive of the long tail.

In the East, particularly in India, the Cheetah is regularly trained for the hunting of deer and antelopes. The hunters bandage the Cheetah's eyes until the moment arrives when it must call all its natural powers into play. When released, the creature sets out in hot pursuit of the game, and with one powerful leap strikes down the selected animal. In order to distract its attention from its captured and legitimate prey, the keepers give it a bowl of hot blood, or the head and neck of a fowl, of which it is extremely fond. Then it is hooded again until more game is in sight.

As we study all these varied forms of animal life, many of them ferocious, and wild, and yet possessing a certain beauty of form combined wth a strange equipment of various weapons for defense and offense, the question arises as to the reason for it all. If the Creator is responsible, what purpose is there in bringing into being predatory animals who live but to destroy? This question is often asked, but I have not the complete answer. I know that most forms of life have some definite use, and probably all forms, originally, were tame and created for the companionship and pleasure of man. When sin entered, the lower animal creation suffered along with everything else, as the curse of God was pronounced.

It is clear from many Bible statements that one day the fierce animal nature will be taken away, and they will revert to their original state. We read in Isaiah 11:6:

> "The wolf also shall dwell with the lamb,
> and the leopard shall lie down with the
> kid; and the calf and the young lion and
> the fatling together; and a little child shall
> lead them . . . and the lion shall eat straw
> like the ox."

What a change that will be from present conditions! Today if the calf and young lion lie down together, the calf is inside the lion!

When, down here, we are tempted to be discouraged at the awful ravages of death—death due to natural causes as well as to that which decimates the population in time of war—it is a comforting thought to know that we are promised a sure Haven of Rest, where peace reigns, where sorrow and trouble and death and crying and tears and suffering shall be no more.

This magnificent prospect is not for every one. That is the point I would have you remember and meditate upon. Are you, my friend, in a position to claim this reward? Only if you have met the one condition, and that condition brings you face to face with Christ. May I present Him to you? Will you come into the inner circle, and enjoy the immeasurable blessings of the present and the infinitely greater joys yet to come in the near future? He waits for your answer.

CHAPTER XXX

THE WORLD'S LARGEST ANIMAL

There is nothing in all today's living world that is in the least like an Elephant. In most respects it stands quite alone. Its huge size, its straight, pillar-like limbs, its short neck, its enormous head, carried quite horizonally, and, above all, its wonderful, elastic, and sensitive trunk—all make of it something to marvel at, an animal that looks as if out of this world, or a survivor of long past ages.

Elephants are now to be found only in the hotter parts of Asia—the Indian jungles, Ceylon, Sumatra, and a few other islands, and in the wilds of Central Africa. Remains of an interesting race of "pigmy" elephants, many of them no larger than a sheep, have been found in the islands of Malta and Cyprus.

The prehistoric form of Elephant, about which we know most, is the Mammoth, which was about the size and type of the Indian Elephant, but was covered with a thick coat of short reddish wool, interspersed with long black hairs. Its bones and teeth have been found all over England, the north of Europe, North America, and in the remotest islands of the Arctic seas. Pictures of it have been found on the walls of caves, and carved by man's hand on the ivory of its own tusks. So abundant are the heaps of bones and teeth in certain locations, that a trade in fossil ivory has been carried on for more than two centuries, for these mammoths bore a fine pair of large, curved tusks.

In addition to these heaps of remains, several whole animals have been found in an upright position, well below the surface of the ground in northern Siberia. They seem to have sunk bodily into a marsh, or to have been suddenly overwhelmed by a landslide, accompanied by a sudden change from a mild climate to one of intense cold. The bodies have been so preserved, in many instances, by being so continuously frozen that no decomposition has set in.

There are two kinds of Elephants, the Indian or Asiatic, and the African. The Indian form is the smaller of the two, but a full-grown male stands from nine to eleven feet high at the shoulders. His great body is covered with a thick, much wrinkled skin, having only a few sparse hairs. The folds of skin afford a favorite feeding ground and hiding-place for many insects, so that the Elephants are often seen with many insect-eating birds on their backs. The birds get quite a comfortable living, and the Elephant is glad to accommodate them because of the comfort and relief they bring from the annoyance of his parasites—unwelcome visitors getting a free ride and a parking-place on the back of the pachyderm.

The Elephant's neck is very powerful, but so short that no great range of movement by the huge head is possible. The head, in turn, must be strong enough to bear the weight of the heavy tusks, and have a large enough surface for the insertion of the great muscles needed to move the trunk.

The animal often uses the bony part of the head above the trunk to push over things, or as a kind of battering-ram. Here we find a strange and evidently designed feature to prevent injury to the brain when using the head in this way. There is a large space more than a foot in extent behind the strong outer layer of bone in front of the brain entirely filled with a network of air-spaces separated by very thin bony plates. Similar aircells are found in the bones of the nose and jaw, and they all communicate with each other, and ultimately with the nostrils, so that air can penetrate all of them. Thus the enormous head is really not so heavy as it looks, and it is not at all a vulnerable part of the animal, for a bullet aimed at the forehead loses itself harmlessly in the labyrinth of air-spaces without entering the brain.

The front "milk" or incisor teeth of the young Elephant are shed at an early age, and their place is taken by the tusks, which go on growing throughout life, and often, in the male, reach a very large size. Those of the female are shorter and less curved. These tusks are made of fine elastic "dentine," with just a tip of enamel which is soon rubbed off. The dentine is the valuable ivory of commerce.

The Elephant uses his tusks for many purposes— rooting up plants, piercing or holding down an enemy, or supporting a heavy weight held in position by the trunk. He is always careful to keep them from being broken. There is no dentist for him, to supply him with any satisfactory substitute, if he breaks one of these important teeth!

The trunk or proboscis gives the Elephant its chief distinction. This wonderful organ is a prolongation of the nose, which, however, takes in part of the upper lip. It is a long, straight tube, divided down the middle, very elastic and mobile, being made up of rings of muscle, very sensitive and well supplied with nerves.

The extremity ends in a finger-like projection, which rivals in delicacy the trained fingers of a blind man.

This trunk serves all the purposes of a hand, an arm, and a lip as well. With it he tears up the juicy plants upon which he loves to feed, and puts them into his mouth; with it, he can break down the branches of a tree and strip them of bark and leaves. If he so desires, he can even trim a branch into a fan and use it to drive off the flies that torment him ceaselessly by day. With it he drinks, filling it with water, curving it around, and squirting the liquid into his mouth. The value of the trunk to the Elephant is almost incredible. He can, with it, pluck a blade of grass, or pick up a minute object from the ground. Without its aid, the huge creature would soon starve; for the short, thick neck would not permit him to graze; the projecting tusks would hinder him from reaching vegetables growing at the level of the mouth; and as water could not be drawn into the mouth without the use of this hose-like trunk, thirst alone would speedily put an end to his existence.

In order to support the enormous weight which rests upon them, the legs are very stout and are set perpendicularly without the joint in the hind leg which is found in most animals. This pillar-like structure is of infinite use when the animal climbs up or down steep places. It does this with marvelous ease. Considering its bulk, the Elephant is remarkably active. It can lie down and regain its feet as easily as a dog; it can stand upon the hind feet alone, or lift itself up on its forefeet; and it can even stand on its head. It cannot trot nor gallop, but when necessary, can travel at a speed of eight or ten miles an hour. Its longest stride is six and a half feet, and it cannot jump

an inch. It is a powerful swimmer and a herd will
cross a broad river, swimming for several hours at a
time with only the tip of the trunk above water.

The Indian Elephant has its home in the great
jungles along the foot of the Himalayas, and elsewhere
throughout India, the Malay Peninsula, and some of
the larger islands. Usually they live in family parties of
twenty to forty, but sometimes several of such herds
unite together for a time. The herd is always under the
leadership of an old "tusker" who demands and receives unquestioning obedience. The females and young
ones lead the way in marching, the males bringing up
the rear.

In spite of their great size and strength, they are
very peaceable among themselves, and towards other
animals and man, whom they rarely attack. Existence
depending largely on his soft and tender trunk, he is
bound to keep the peace with all creatures. He takes the
greatest care of this organ, knowing apparently that
he cannot live without it.

Elephants are wholly vegetarian, and although
they have their favorite food-plants, nothing in the
way of grasses, leaves or even young branches comes
amiss to them. Herds of Elephants are constantly in
search of new feeding grounds. Usually they march
after dark, and may travel far up the mountain sides.
They climb very skillfully and carefully, the leader
testing every rock and tree-trunk, the rest following in
single file.

Whether in the plains or on the mountain sides, the
one thing that seems absolutely indispensable is abundant water for drinking and bathing.

A female Elephant usually has one calf every two

years. This baby is about three feet high at birth, and continues to grow for twenty-five years. It sucks with the mouth in the usual way, keeping the trunk folded back. The calf develops rapidly and a few hours after birth is able to move along with the herd. At first it walks directly in front of the mother who guides it by laying her trunk along its back, but when a little stronger, the calf runs under her body, and will always retreat there on the slightest alarm. In swimming, the young one is either supported by the trunk of the mother, or may be carried more conveniently on her back.

The African Elephant is a good deal larger than his Asiatic cousins. His ears cover a much greater area, his tusks are heavier and rather more curved, while his trunk has two finger-like projections, one at either end.

One thing which strikes us in our survey of animals in general is the endless variety in construction, in size, in instincts, in manner of life, and various other features. But there are always certain things held in common. All animals have the desire to live, even if it be at the expense of others. Most animals exhibit real solicitude towards their young. All mothers are equipped with the necessary bodily parts required for feeding the more or less helpless young. The newly born animals know where to go for nourishment and exactly what to do to get it. The anatomical arrangement of bones, muscles, joints and organs, is of greatest interest, each animal having its own peculiar and special gifts adapted to its needs and environment. All these things indicate a Power above and beyond the animal itself, because they come into existence with all these powers ready to be utilized. And this must have been true from the very beginning.

We are constantly driven back to our first conclusion, "In the beginning God created." The evidence of a Creator is so abundant and conclusive that one can scarcely understand the attempt to shelve this Omnipotent Source of all things, and to be satisfied with a wholly imaginary and inoperative theory which prefers to accept the most astonishing miracles in anatomical change without any miraculous Power to bring them about. Of course, Creation is a miracle. We do not deny that, but rather derive much satisfaction from the conviction that such a Power is needed, and that this Power has manifested Himself in most unmistakable ways.

Personally, I am more thankful every day for the knowledge I have of God, and for the revelation of Jesus Christ. Why should I be ashamed of Him? With Paul we can say, "I am not ashamed of the Gospel of Christ, for it is the power of God." But only "unto him that believeth." Are you getting an added sense of God's greatness and love? I do hope you are receiving a real thrill as these great truths are being unfolded from day to day, and that there is reality in His presence.

CHAPTER XXXI

THE LONGEST NOSE IN THE WORLD

Before we begin the study of birds, I think I shall ask you to look with me at some remarkable features of animal construction in relation to apparent defects in one part or organ, this defect compensated by the peculiar structure of another part or organ. It is not possible to imagine any stronger evidence of planning than this survey will give us.

We have been thinking of the Elephant, and the Bat, and other animals, each with strange equipment and powers, and we shall see many more. Let us again spend a moment or two with the Elephant.

The short unbending neck is compensated by the length and flexibility of the trunk or proboscis. He could not have reached the ground without it; or, if it be supposed that he might have fed on the fruit, leaves, or branches of trees, how was he to drink? And we know that water is absolutely indispensable in large quantities to his Mammoth.

If we ask, "Why is the Elephant's neck so short?" the answer is that the weight of a head so heavy could not have been supported at the end of a long lever. Consequently, a supplement is added which exactly makes up the deficiency under which he would have labored.

If it be suggested that this proboscis may have been produced through a long series of generations by the constant attempts of the Elephant to thrust out his nose, we ask the natural question, How was the animal to exist in the meantime, during the process, UNTIL this prolongation of the snout be completed? What was to become of the individual while the anatomical changes were being evolved? Undoubtedly, there would be speedy death to every Elephant.

I am trying to point out the relation which this organ bears to the peculiar figure of the animal, and to its mode of obtaining food to supply its bulky frame; which is not only by browsing on grass, but also on the foliage of trees. And here all things correspond.

The need for the Elephant's proboscis arises from the shortness of his neck; the shortness of the neck is rendered necessary by the weight of the head. This long nasal projection is one of the most curious of all examples of animal mechanism. As we have seen, it is tubular, endowed with enormous muscular power, and with the most delicate sensitiveness at its extremity. With it its possessor can gather food, rend large branches of trees, or with the delicate finger-like end, pick up a straw or a penny. It is the hand by which food and drink are conveyed to the mouth, and the pump with which it can syringe its huge body. It is also a weapon of defense with which it can crush in its powerful grasp whatever it seizes; or hurl an enemy to the ground, to be gored with its long tusks, or trampled to death beneath its ponderous feet.

These properties—all found in this one organ— taken together, exhibit not only design of the most marked character, but consummate art, and elaborate preparation in accomplishing that design.

We have examined the Bat. The hook in the wing of this mammal is a mechanical, and also a compensating contrivance. At the angle of its wing, attached to its short thumb, there is a bent nail or claw, exactly in the form of a hook, by which the Bat attaches itself to the sides of rocks, caves, and buildings, laying hold of crevices, chinks, and slight projections. It hooks itself by this claw; remains suspended by it; and takes its flight from this position. It is easily seen that this strange device compensates for the inability of the legs to assist in standing or walking. These lacks or failures —if we care to call them such—are made up to it by the wing contrivance in the form of the hook. In placing a claw on that part, the Creator has deviated from that which is observed in winged animals, but has thus supplied it with the means of roosting in safety.

Anticipating a little the study of birds, let us think for a moment of a Crane, a bird created to live and seek its food among the waters. Cranes have no webbed feet and so are incapable of swimming. To make up for this lack, they are furnished with long legs for wading, or long bills for groping, or, usually, with both. This again is compensation.

The tongues of birds are not constructed as organs of taste, which sense, as we shall see, is imperfectly developed in this class. Birds are specially employed in obtaining and preparing their food for swallowing. For this purpose, the tongue is supported by two small bones extending upward from the hyoid, a U-shaped bone at the base of the tongue. The tongue also is provided with a thick horny covering.

In the parrot, the tongue can be opposed to the hooked upper jaw, as our thumb is to the fingers. In birds which feed on honey, the tip of the tongue is given a feathery tuft, like a camel's-hair brush, by which it gathers its food. The tongue of the woodpecker is prolonged into a sharp lance, by which it reaches and pierces its prey—an arrangement aided by the very sticky saliva poured out beneath the point of the tongue. The parrot's beak is not adapted for picking up grain, but is strong enough to crush hard substances, and the hook in it helps admirably in climbing.

The spider's web is a compensating contrivance. The spider lives on flies, but has no wings to pursue them. This seems to present the spider with an insurmountable difficulty, but the resourcefulness of the Creator of the spider, without any thinking or effort of the animal, overcomes this handicap in a most delightful and successful fashion. We shall examine it later.

In many species of insects, the eye is fixed, and so without the power of turning in the direction of the object to be looked at. However, this great defect is perfectly compensated by a curious mechanism. The eye becomes a magnifying glass with a lense looking in every direction, enabling the retina to catch rays from every object.

In the eyes of flies, butterflies, and other insects, the field of vision is enlarged by the presence of thousands of six-sided facets, each a perfect eye, with cornea, lens, iris and pupil. This is surely not the result of any possible chance operation.

In the chameleon, instead of there being two eyelids, the eye is covered with one eyelid with a hole in it. This, as we shall see, is wonderfully compensatory. The neck of this animal in inflexible, and to make up for this, the eye is so prominent that half of the eye ball stands out of the head. By means of this extraordinary projection, the pupil of the eye can be carried by the muscles in every direction, and each eye, separately, is capable of being pointed toward any object. On one side, the chameleon looks in one direction, and on the opposite side in an entirely different direction. The unusual exposure of the globe of the eye is dangerous, so an additional protection is required to prevent injury, and provision must be made for plenty of moisture. So what do we find? The pronounced convexity of this projecting organ makes it impossible to use an eyelid formed according to the general plan, so the aperture in the single lid meets the difficulty. The principal part of the eye may be kept covered, and constant moisture is possible. Where, at first glance, we notice apparent defects, we always come upon some notable contrivance to supply what is lacking.

A Snail, without wings, feet, or thread, climbs up the stalks of plants by the aid of a sticky secretion manufactured in its skin. It easily adheres to the stems, leaves, and fruits of plants by means of this adhesive plaster!

A Fly can walk on the ceiling because it has suckers on its feet.

The Mussel, a small bi-valve mollusk, seems to be very helpless, and at the mercy of every wave that touches it; but it has been equipped with the ability to spin strong tendinous threads by which it moors its shell to rocks and timbers.

A Lobster, when we examine it, seems to be hopelessly handicapped for increasing its size. The Lobster's shell is a protecting covering and is also an attachment for muscles. It is too hard to expand with increasing growth of the Lobster, so the shell must be discarded or the animal will be squeezed to death. How can it extricate itself from its confinement? How can it un-case its buckler, or draw its legs out of its boots?

Usually in the autumn, the animal retires to a se-cluded place where the shell loosens, as a soft cover-ing develops beneath the old shell. It works desperate-ly, and by tremulous spasmodic motions, casts off the shell, and then withdraws the legs from their casing. The now defenseless animal retires to a hole in a near-by rock, while a new and larger shell of the proper size to accommodate it grows and develops and hardens in a few days.

The shells of crustaceans are very brittle and limbs are easily broken and detached—a most serious complication, one would think. This defect is com-pensated by another remarkable provision, which makes possible the production of an entirely new limb in place of the one lost. Examples like these are num-berless, and I think I shall devote our next session to a further study of these phenomena. They are surely interesting.

I know from your letters that very many of you are fascinated with these discussions and the evidence they provide for a personal God. I am delighted with the response, and am sure that this conviction in your minds that there must be an intelligent Creator is proving vastly comforting and exciting.

This is the great truth mentioned hundreds of times in the Bible. We cannot, we MUST not ignore it. If we do—and we have ignored it in the past as a nation—we must expect judgment of the severest kind. We are now in the midst of a devastating war. A world is dying. Many causes are assigned, and people con-stantly ask why God permits such insane destruction

of life. It is argued that an omnipotent Creator, righteous and holy and peace-loving—if there be such a
Being—has apparently forgotten this world or does
not care. The question comes, "Why does He not put
an immediate stop to the carnage?"

Friends, God did not bring on this war. It is caused
by the sin of mankind — universal and defiant sin.
There is but one way out and that is the way of con-
fession and humiliation—a way which unregenerate
nations are loath to travel. God's warnings have been
disregarded, and the result is terror and death from
vicious enemies.

In Amos 3:10, 11, are these words: "They know not
to do right . . . THEREFORE thus saith the Lord: An
adversary shall there be even round about the land;
and he shall bring down thy strength from thee, and
thy dwelling-places shall be spoiled."

Oh, yes, the Allied Nations will win the war—but
they will win the hard way. Why not seek an alliance
with the one Power that could and would bring immediate victory?

Individually, we may protect ourselves against danger and death. I offer you an insurance policy that
gives you immediate and everlasting promise of victory and peace and joy through time and eternity. You
know where you can secure it—from the outstretched
hand of the Man of Calvary—the Christ of Golgotha.
Will you turn His way today? He's wonderful.

CHAPTER XXXII

HOW NATURE CLOTHES HER CHILDREN

In our last session we were thinking of some of the curious examples of compensation seen in animals. That is, some animals seem to lack parts which, in our opinion, might be absolutely necessary if they are to carry on with any degree of comfort or success. In all these instances, we have discovered that they have been given compensatory parts or organs, which operate quite satisfactorily in the absence of those parts found in other animals. In other words, the Creator is able to bring about the same desired result in many different ways.

Think for a moment of the COVERING of different animals. This covering varies greatly, but is always suited to each animal, and meets its special need perfectly. There are bristles, hair, wool, fur, feathers, quills, prickles, and scales. If we had the power to change this covering, in individual instances, it would always be for the worse. It may be stated here, that these various coverings in many cases serve as armor as well as clothing, for protection as well as for warmth.

Man is the only mammal that is naked, and the only one that has the power to clothe himself. Thus he is able to live in all climates, and at all seasons, because he can adapt his covering to the temperature requirements. If we were born with a thick coat of fleece, it would be a source of comfort in cold climates, and a great saving in clothing, but how oppressive would be its heat and weight in warmer regions.

So, what art has done for man, Nature has done for animals incapable of art. Their clothing, of its own accord, changes with the necessity of the season. Animals with a covering of fur do not have to plan change of raiment. When winter approaches, the fur grows much thicker; and when spring returns, the weight of the fur is diminished.

It is interesting to note that bears, wolves, foxes, hares, and the like, that do not take to the water, have their fur much thicker on the back than underneath; whereas, animals like the beaver, have a much thicker coat in the abdominal region than on the back.

The covering of birds must not escape our observation. There are so many interesting features here—its lightness, its smoothness, its warmth, the disposition of the feathers, all inclined backward, the downy covering of the stem, the overlapping of their tips, their different arrangement in different parts, the variety of colors. All this constitutes a vestment for the body of the bird, so beautiful and perfect that we can imagine nothing to equal it.

And, by the way, every feather is a mechanical wonder—the quill, strong, and light, and hollow, tapering to a fine point with a geometrical precision accurate to the millionth part of an inch. It is tough, light, pliant, elastic—exactly what is needed. The barbs and barbules on the sides of the quill are remarkable structures. We all know that when these tiny barbules are pulled apart, they resist our efforts slightly; and when we remove our fingers, they snap back to their original position. Examined with a magnifying glass, you will find that these parts of the feather have been equipped with infinitely small locks — thousands of them, the parts fitting into one another with a beautiful precision which baffles description. On a large feather, it has been pointed out that there are more than a million of these perfect locks.

To small birds, the Creator gave a bed of soft down, next to their bodies. This down retains air, a bad conductor of heat, and so they are kept warm.

A study of the mouths of various animals reveals some strange devices. The mouth is used to receive food, to catch prey, to pick up seeds, to crop herbs, to extract juices, to suck liquids, to break and grind food, to taste it, and also is intended to assist in respiration and the utterance of sound. These various offices in different species are performed in different ways or with a variation in structure which is amazing.

Because we have hands to convey food to the mouth, our mouth is flat, and designed only for reception; whereas, the dog, for instance, has projecting jaws and pointed teeth which enable him to apply his mouth to snatch and seize the objects of his pursuit. The ox, the deer, the horse, and sheep need to browse upon their pasture. Accordingly, they have full lips, rough tongue, a corrugated, cartilaginous palate, and broad cutting teeth, so, where the grass is long, they gather large mouthfuls at once, and where the grass is short, they can bite close.

Have you noticed the retiring under-jaw of the pig, which works in the ground after the protruding snout, like a prong or ploughshare, has made its way to the roots upon which it feeds?

In birds, the mouth assumes a new character, both in substance and form, wonderfully well adapted to the wants and uses of their mode of existence. No longer do we see fleshy lips, or teeth of enamel and dentine. Instead, we see a hard substance cut into proper shapes, and mechanically suited to the needed actions—the bill.

The sparrow's bill, with its sharp edge and tempered point, enables it to pick up every kind of seed it wants. With it, the sparrow hulls the grain, breaks and shatters the coats of the seed, to get at the kernel. The hooked beak of the hawk separates the flesh from the bones of the animal upon which it feeds with the cleanness of precision of a dissector's knife. The spoon-bill of the goose makes it easy to collect food from the bottom of pools among the soft or liquid substances mixed with it. The snipe and the woodcock have long tapering bills which can penetrate deep into the moist earth where the food is lodged. It is exactly the instrument needed. They need length rather than strength which conforms also to the slender neck, and are provided with a perfect tool.

Some birds live by suction, and have what are known as serrated bills, the inside of which, toward the edge, are thickly set with rows of short, strong, sharp-pointed prickles. These are not for the purpose of mastication, like the teeth of mammals; nor yet are they, as in fish, for seizing and retaining their pray. They have an entirely different use. They form a filter.

The duck, for instance, penetrates the puddle of mud or whatever mixture is likely to contain its food. By suction it draws the liquid or semi-liquid substances through the narrow gaps lying between these prickles, which we might call teeth, for want of a better name. As the stream passes across its beak, it separates what it wants and discharges the rest. What more could the duck want than this natural filter?

Everything about the animal mouth is mechanical. The teeth of fish have their points turning backward; the teeth of lobsters work one against another, like the sides of a pair of shears. In many insects, the mouth is converted into a pump or sucker, fitted at one end with a gimlet arrangement, sometimes with a forceps, so they are able to bore through and extract the juices on which they live.

Whether it be lips or teeth, or bill or beak, or shears or pump, it is always the same part, changed to suit the special animal. Under all the variations in construction, the organs of taste and smell are situated near each other. If the odor is offensive, we humans will not taste — or will we? What about limburger cheese? Odors which are repellent to humans are often very much liked by animals.

In quadrupeds, the absence of certain teeth is usually accompanied by the faculty of rumination, where the food is swallowed, and then returned to the mouth to be chewed over again and swallowed again while the digestion is completed in another compartment of the stomach. The sheep, deer and ox-tribe are without front teeth in the upper jaw, and so they ruminate.

Birds have no teeth with which to grind their food, but are furnished with the gizzard, the inner coat of which is fitted with hard, rough plaits or folds. By powerful rubbing against one another, they break and grind the hard food substances, making it easy then for the gastric secretion to digest them. Without this unique grinding-machine inside its body, all the common fowls, such as turkeys, ducks, geese, pigeons, etc., would have starved to death, even though surrounded and filled with unbroken grain kernels. A bill and a gizzard go together, and a gizzard is never found where there are teeth. A gizzard is not found in birds of prey, because their food does not require grinding in a mill.

Some animals have no feet. How is this lack compensated for? Snakes can move rapidly because of the way the muscles and tissues of the trunk are constructed. Their rapid zig-zag movement is made possible by the arrangement of their scaly covering, and the wonderful mobility of their ball-and-socket jointed vertebrae and ribs.

The lowly earthworm has a body made up of a series of rings and moves with a curious undulatory motion, aided by prickly hairs on the surface of its body, which this animal can pull in close to itself or thrust out and lay hold on the rough surface over which it creeps, this strange muscular action working admirably to make possible this method of locomotion.

There is no end to observations like these. I have brought them to your attention in order that you may catch a glimpse of Omniscience. Do you not see some of God's wisdom and power in all these astonishing adaptations at which we have looked? And, particularly are you not struck with the infinite thoughtfulness of the Creator? Everything that animals need is in their possession when they come into existence, contrivances which exacty fit the needs of each specimen.

Is it to be wondered at when the Psalmist exclaims in Psalm 31:19: "Oh, how great is Thy goodness which Thou hast laid up for them that fear Thee; which Thou hast wrought for them that trust in Thee before the sons of men."

Here is the goodness of God prepared and kept in store, or "laid up," as the Psalmist puts it, for a certain group—"them that fear Thee," and also for them that manifest their faith in God "before the sons of men."

A faith, which is ashamed to express itself vocally before men, is not acceptable to God. He desires that we offer our worship and praise in the presence of those who may be inclined to smile superciliously at our simple trust in God. We are daily recipients of His bounty. Why not thank Him? Do you think it childish and fanatical to pause a moment at meals and express thanks for the food provided? When we realize our complete dependence on God for everything we enjoy, we shall be glad to express our thanks. We are courteous to our friends—but to God how different is the attitude of many otherwise gracious people. Will you think it over? We have a wonderful Saviour! Do you know Him?

CHAPTER XXXIII

THE ANIMAL THAT CARRIES ITS OWN WATER TANK

We cannot think of the desert without thinking of the Camel. Here is a strange creature, which alone of all animals, can exist among desert conditions of dust, heat, and lack of water. We cannot evade the conclusion that God planned this mammal especially for man's use in the desert places of the earth.

There are two kinds—the Arabian with one hump, and the Bactrian with two humps. Apart from the difference in humps, which are curious appendages of fat, they are alike in general form, habits, and usefulness.

From the earliest times this ungainly-looking animal has been subjected to man, and in Eastern countries has always contributed much to the comfort, wealth, and influence of its owner.

The Arabian Camel is about seven feet high at the shoulder, or nine feet to the top of the head, which is set on a long, curved neck. The animal is intended to traverse parched and sandy plains, and so its feet are specially prepared. They are fitted with wide, soft cushions, which are well adapted for walking on loose dry sand. With these flat cushion-like pads it shuffles across the desert and stays on top of the sand.

The Creator knew this animal would be required to kneel while heavy loads were placed on its back, and so the knees are furnished with thick, callous pads, so that there is little fear of injury while it takes the necessary position for loading. Many people think these pads are developed by pressure, but that is not the case. The young camels are born with them.

The humps are fatty deposits which give the Camel a good reserve of food for a desert journey where little nourishment is possible. When the animals return from their desert trips, these humps are much reduced in size, flapping across the back, giving quite a changed appearance to the starving desert-traveler. They are speedily restored by a course of ample feeding and the animal is ready for another period of fasting.

Also noteworthy are the water reservoirs in the wall of the paunch, about 800 little flasks with a closing muscle around the mouth of each. They are filled with water automatically when the Camel slakes his thirst. In time of water scarcity the stored liquid is allowed to trickle into the stomach and is available for the blood, impoverished of fluid. This device makes for great endurance. The story is told of a hundred well-loaded camels journeying for thirteen consecutive days with absolutely no fresh water. And Prof. J. W. Gregory cites a case from Australia, where some of the naturalized Camels were marched 537 miles in thirty-four days without watering.

The deserts are frequently the scenes of terrible sandstorms, but the eyes of the camel are heavily lidded, and the large nostrils have special muscles which can close them at will, thus preventing the sand from entering.

In its native land the Camel is almost invariably employed as a pack animal, and it can support a load of five or six hundred pounds with considerable ease. The term "dromedary" is applied only to the lighter breed of animals. These creatures are completely equipped for their strange life, and face the desert sands with boldness, traversing the hot, arid wastes with an easy celerity that has gained for them the title "Ship of the Desert."

The fastest speed of a Camel is about eight to ten miles an hour, but it can keep this up for twenty hours without stopping, and it can maintain a rate of seventy or eighty miles a day for nearly a week.

To the uninitiated, camel-riding is neither easy nor comfortable. The rider mounts while the animal is kneeling, and sits like the women of other years who rode "side-saddle." In rising, the Camel suddenly straightens its hind legs so that, if the rider is unprepared, he is jerked over its ears. It moves with a long undulating motion, swaying to and fro from its loins, in addition to which, it has an annoying habit of swerving from the track to snatch at any drab-colored plant which it may happen to pass.

As a result of the fitness of Camels, man has made them his slave, but all work and little or no play seems to have made them somewhat cantankerous. They appear to protest continually, grumbling and growling, biting, and kicking. Perhaps they have cultivated illtemper until it has become a form of enjoyment for them. They are morose and rancorous in disposition, always ready to bite; and as soon as unloaded, they promptly engage in vicious combats with their own species.

In addition to being a beast of burden, the Camel supplies its owner with food and clothing. Its milk, mixed with meal, is a favorite dish, especially when it is sour. A rancid butter is also churned from the cream by a very primitive process, the cream being poured into a goatskin sack, and then shaken constantly until the butter is formed. The long hair of the Camel, which it sheds at certain periods of the year, is spun into coarse thread for the manufacture of cloth.

Man gives the animal little affection in spite of its usefulness, and this feeling is reciprocated. The Camel carries its head high, and thus the eyes are removed from the ground-reflected heat, but this attitude gives it an air of bored contempt. It ruminates—that is, chews its cud, and when thus engaged, it sometimes seems as if preoccupied with some precious thought, such as this, perhaps—that they are the only mammals whose red blood cells are oval or elliptical in shape.

.   In all its features the Camel was created to bear burdens and to serve mankind in desert places. Our thought is turned to another Bearer of burdens, the One who came to earth to bear our load of sin. Here is what Peter says about it in his first Epistle 2:24: "Who his own self bare our sins in his own body on the tree, that we, being dead to sins, should live unto righteousness: by whose stripes ye were healed."

But He took more than our sins. His love prompted Him to share all our troubles. Isa. 53:4 tells us that "Surely He hath borne our grief and carried our sorrows."

We have just been thinking of the Camel. Someone has written about the "Lesson of the Camel."

> "The camel at the close of day
> Kneels down upon the sandy plain
> To have his burden lifted off,
> And rest to gain.

My soul—thou too, shouldst to thy knees,
When daylight draweth to a close,
And let the Master lift thy load,
And grant repose.

Else how couldst thou tomorrow meet
With all tomorrow's work to do,
If thou thy burden all the night
Dost carry through?

The camel kneels at break of day,
To have his guide replace his load,
Then rises up anew to take
The desert road.

So thou shouldst kneel at morning's dawn,
That God may give thee daily care
Assured that He no load too great
Will make thee bear."

Ofttimes we are very weary with the load we carry; we become discouraged and depressed; we are almost ready to give up the fight. Have any of you who listen to me ever had that experience? I'm sure you have. Here are some comforting lines about this problem.

It is good to be weary for so we seek rest,
And we find it at last as we lean on His
        breast;
It is well to be lonely for thus we may
        prove
That this Saviour can fill every void with
        His love.

It is good to be weak so that thus we may
        turn
To the Strong One for help, and His

mightiness learn;
It is well if we find that the desert is drear.
It is thus we are taught that our home is
    not here.

It is good when our burdens are heavy to
    bear,
If they send us to Him and they drive us to
    prayer,
Every need is a boon, every sorrow is blest,
When it leads us to put His great love to
    the test.

Phillips Brooks wrote a little poem, "Our Burden Bearer." Listen to it:

The little sharp vexations
And the briers that catch and fret,
Why not take all to the Helper
Who has never failed us yet?
Tell Him about the heartache,
And tell Him the longings, too;

Tell Him the baffled purpose
When we scarce know what to do.
Then leaving all our weakness
With the One Divinely strong,
Forget that we bore the burden,
And carry away the song.

The Bible abounds with remarkable statements regarding God's willingness and desire to assist us in the battle of life—to make living as easy and pleasant as possible. He wants us to be happy, and without exception those who have accepted God's challenge and have joined company with Him, have rejoiced at the astonishing results.

I would like to let the Bible speak for itself. Will you hear some of its great words?

> (Ps. 27:1) "The Lord is my light and my salvation; whom shall I fear? The Lord is the strength of my life; of whom shall I be afraid?"

> (Ps. 37:39) "But the salvation of the righteous is of the Lord: He is their strength in the time of trouble."

> (Isa. 12:2) "Behold, God is my salvation; I will trust, and not be afraid: for the Lord Jehovah is my strength and my song; He also is become my salvation."

> (Isa. 25:9) "And it shall be said in that day, Lo, this is our God; we have waited for Him, and He will save us: this is the Lord, we have waited for Him; we will be glad and rejoice in His salvation."

> (Zeph. 3:17) "The Lord thy God in the midst of thee is mighty; He will save, He will rejoice over thee with joy; He will rest in His love, He will joy over thee in singing."

All these varied benefits, which are assured to those to whom the promises come, are, if true, of great moment. Can every one claim God's protection and care and blessing? There is a loose way of thinking today which seems to take for granted that any one, in time of trouble or distress, can utter a cry for help, and God is bound to come immediately to the rescue. Then, the one who has prayed seems to think that, after the crisis is past, he may again forget all about God until the next crisis.

This attitude reveals an entirely mistaken view of the situation. You will have noticed that all the promises of help are to God's children—to those who are members of His family and so can call Him "Father." We hear much of the Fatherhood of God and the Brotherhood of Man. The terms are not founded on Truth. God is not the Father of all, nor are all men brothers. God is Creator of all, but to become His children and have the right to address Him in the new and glorious capacity of Father, with all that word implies, requires a new birth. Jesus said, "Ye must be born again." We were born once, but the Bible tells us we were "born in sin" and "were by nature children of wrath." So, a new process of "birth" is necessary to change us from children of the Devil to children of God. Those who have undergone this transformation are then brethren but not before—"heirs of God and joint-heirs with Jesus Christ."

In brief simple words, we must take Jesus as Saviour, relinquishing our old self and permitting Him to be Master of our lives. Then, He becomes our great Burden-bearer. Friend, is the load heavy? Are you staggering under its weight? Let Him have it. Then straighten your shoulders and know the joy of being a free man in Christ. Will you?

CHAPTER XXXIV

THE MAN THE BIBLE CALLS A FOOL

We have now had many talks on various scientific wonders. I think it is time to survey the subject of Atheism, seeing that all our argument has been directed to the fact of a personal God. So, if you will permit me, I will talk today on "The Folly of Atheism."

The most characteristic feature of this sin-stricken world is its refusal to acknowledge God. This blasphemous attitude is not solely the prerogative of those self-styled atheists who blatantly and impudently deny the existence of any Supreme Being possessing personality. It applies also, even if in lesser degree, to the rank and file of humanity. Judging from the abundantly available evidence at our disposal, the majority exhibit little inclination toward any real recognition of God, and comparatively few desire fellowship with Him.

Where can we find a nation that pays more than empty lip service to God? Confronted with the greatest crisis since the dawn of history and threatened with imminent destruction, our leaders occasionally mention the name of God in a hazy, indefinite, apologetic manner. It is a futile gesture reflecting a somewhat disturbing and almost submerged conviction that somewhere there may be a Supreme Being, and it might be well to offer this slight recognition of the fact.

What a surprising shock it would be if any government official occupying high office would have the courage to say a word in behalf of the "Lord Jesus Christ"!

About the only time the world mentions this holy name is in swearing and blasphemy. The only possible end to this defiant challenge to the Savior of the world is judgment sure and terrible when God's wrath breaks on a Christ-rejecting universe.

The extent of the permeation of our higher institutions of learning with atheism is shown by Dr. James H. Leuba of Bryn Mawr College in his book, "Belief in God and Immortality," containing the results of a widespread questionnaire sent by him to hundreds of professors and an equally large number of students. His statistics are probably near to the truth and, if so, are tragically suggestive as to the elimination of God by these men and their students.

Of the great number of replies received he finds the following percentage of avowed atheists:

Psychologists	86%
Biologists	82%
Sociologists	81%
Historians	68%
Physicists	66%

He finds that between forty per cent and fifty per cent of the students, on graduating, reject the idea of God. It is easy to understand this wreckage of faith after four years of teaching by men who make no secret of their atheism.

Because God cannot be seen by mortal vision, men are prone to conclude that He does not exist. Certain sophisticated individuals proclaim vehemently that they will believe only what they can see. Lallande, the astronomer, once said: "I have swept the entire heavens with my telescope and I have found no God." Therefore, he argued, there is no such Being.

How foolish to draw any such inference from the very limited evidence supplied by a telescope. God cannot be discovered by any such mechanical device, but the eye of faith will soon find Him.

The unbeliever depends trustfully on the scope and accuracy of his five senses. He attributes to them great powers. What they reveal he will accept; what they do not disclose he will reject.

One thing that strikes me forcibly is that the skeptic must have acquired a pronounced faith in the clarity of his intellect and in the infallibility of his senses. When we examine them, however, we discover their obvious limitations.

We have eyes. Well, what do we see? The range of visible light is very narrow. Our eyes can run the gamut from the short waves of violet to the long waves of red. There are waves beyond violet and waves beyond red which are invisible to us—two infinite worlds of color above and below these points that are completely hidden from our gaze. Shall we dare to say they do not exist because we cannot see them? Our sense of sight, then, is far from infallible.

There is sound. We have two ears to catch a little of it. The ear can hear vibrations as musical notes only between certain limits. A single vibration produces the sound of a tap or blow, and each vibration is heard as a separate tap or blow until sixteen more occur in every second of time. Then a continuous sound results, the vibrations of which are not separable to the sense of hearing.

The lowest note on the organ is usually produced by a pipe sixteen feet long which gives thirty-two vibrations per second. This note is named C'''. An eight-foot pipe gives its octave with sixty-four vibrations—C''. The double octave C' has 128 vibrations in a second and so on. The highest audible note is said to have about 40,000 vibrations a second but is too feeble to have any musical value. So we hear sounds produced by vibrations of 20 to 40,000 per second.

Beyond and at each end are vast worlds of silence. There are untold numbers of sound waves that our ears cannot detect despite megaphones and amplifiers. Our ears then are far from being infallible guides to sound waves.

The senses of touch, taste and smell have the same marked limitations, the existing faculties scarcely touching these vast shores.

Our minds cannot grasp the mysteries of time and space. We are totally unable to understand eternity—that, actually, time had no beginning and will have no ending. Our imagination staggers when we think of infinite and immeasurable space. If we are to find God with these senses of ours, then we shall be doomed to failure.

There are other phases to this discussion. We are endowed with appetites and longings. We are hungry —there is food. We have the instinct to love—there are those to love. We are eager for power and wealth —they are to be had. For every single desire there is a possible fulfilment.

Put a potato plant in the dark cellar. It is born with the instinct that there is sunlight to be found and so there is. Accordingly the vine searches until it finds the rays from the sun—the rays necessary for its life and growth.

Yes, the lowly potato plant responds to the invitation of light and reaches up to contact it. The result of this meeting is life and growth and progress. The Bible calls our attention to light many times. Listen to some of these words.

"The Lord is my light and my salvation; whom shall I fear? The Lord is the strength of my life; of whom shall I be afraid?" (Ps. 27:1.)

"Blessed is the people that know the joyful sound: they walk, O Lord, in the light of Thy countenance." (Ps. 89:15.)
"The path of the righteous is as the dawning light, that shineth more and more unto the perfect day. The way of the wicked is as darkness; they know not at what they stumble." (Prov. 4:18, 19.)
"The people that walked in darkness have seen a great light; they that dwelt in the land of the shadow of death upon them hath the light shined." (Isa. 9:2.)

There is a word from Jesus Christ, Himself, to which we must listen:

"I am the light of the world: he that followeth me shall not walk in darkness, but shall have the light of life." (John 8: 12.)

How did the world act toward Jesus Christ? The Gospel of John has much to say about it. God is speaking in chapter 1 at the first verse:

"In the beginning was the Word, and the Word was with God, and the Word was

> God . . . In Him was life; and the life was
> the light of men. And the light shineth
> in the darkness; and the darkness compre-
> hended it not."

The world of the first century that turned away from this GREAT LIGHT is no different from our world. This age of ours is steeped in darkness—the utter blackness of sin. Light is available but men and women prefer to walk in darkness, stumbling and falling and refusing the Hand that is held out to them. In the vegetable world we have seen the effect of light and how in this realm all living things bend every energy to reach its rays. But man, wilful and sinning, refuses the only way out. What will the end be? Our age is heading for the abyss and there's but one remedy. This remedy is not man-made. No League of Nations, no peace pacts, no effort which does not take God into account will ever succeed in bringing order to this chaotic universe. God has a plan for the world—one that will work. He offers it but His offer is spurned. It is rejected because it involves subjection to Jesus Christ. It seems that the patience of God is about exhausted. If the world refuses to listen, the world is going to get hurt. And who will dare to say that this punishment is not deserved?

As with nations, so with individuals. Salvation is a very personal thing. Every one must for himself make the decision. This decision is either for or against the Christ of Calvary. Before you or I can get to heaven we must be clothed with righteousness. That is the law of God. I am very sure I cannot make myself righteous, and I know you cannot. What shall we do about it? There is a wonderful plan. Here it is in Romans 4:5:

"To him that worketh not, but believeth on

Him that justifieth the ungodly, HIS
FAITH IS RECKONED FOR RIGHT-
EOUSNESS."

As for me, I have believed, and in the sight of God,
I am as righteous as Jesus Christ, because His right-
eousness becomes mine. Easy, isn't it? Will you take
Him today? He's a wonderful Saviour.

CHAPTER XXXV

WHAT SCIENTISTS THINK ABOUT GOD

Continuing our subject, "The Man the Bible Calls a Fool" or "The Folly of Atheism," which I discussed in the last broadcast, some additional observations may be offered.

There is no savage tribe, no civilized race, that has not searched for God and longed for immortality. It is the earliest, deepest and most passionate desire of mankind. All other desires and instincts have an answer. Will this innate consciousness and longing for God be forever denied? It is incredible.

This instinct, this emotion, this belief—call it what you will—is more powerful than any other. It has conquered love, and even the fear of death. It has built civilizations. It has set the spires of churches in the valleys around the world.

If this be a fable, it is a mighty tough one to kill. They wrote it off the books in the French Revolution, but it soon sneaked in at the back door. They liquidated it in Russia, but it is filtering in again. They buried it in the catacombs of Rome, but it escaped and soon covered the earth. They crucified it; it was born again, rising into newness of life and vigor, victorious over death and the grave.

In the crises of life men turn instinctively toward God. Several months ago Brigadier General William R. Arnold, chief of the chaplains of the Army of the United States, released a story from his voluminous files, producing evidence of the reaction of a soldier to the screaming shadows of death falling from the skies. He tells the experience of Lieut.-Col. Warren Clear on Bataan.

The Colonel, who was never an habitual church-goer, leaped into a fox-hole in the midst of an intense bombardment from the air. A sergeant squeezed over to make room. When explosions opened the earth and ripped trees roundabout, the noncom prayed aloud without any shame. Words forgotten since childhood soon came to the officer's lips, as he echoed his companion's prayer for divine protection.

After the enemy planes had passed over, Clear remarked more to himself than to his companion, "We prayed!" "Yes," replied the other quite casually, "we did. There are no atheists in fox-holes."

This is but an echo of the statement in Psalm 14: "The fool hath said in his heart, There is no God." The fact of God is the basis of all logical thinking, the foundation of any rational conception of the origin of things, the only hope for individuals or nations in time or eternity. God is the only scientific and satisfying explanation of the universe and all things therein.

An infidel science boasts that it needs no God. In His place it places evolution which satisfies neither mind nor spirit.

The believer in Creation and God is sometimes ridiculed because he accepts the supernatural. The sophisticated scientific infidel professes to reject anything which savors of miracle, and confidently appeals to Natural Law.

Will he then be good enough to explain to me by natural law how I can send an electric current through a copper wire at sixty degrees below zero, and at the other end heat a platinum wire to thousands of degrees? Where was that heat? From whence did it come?

A storage battery weighing fifty pounds, fully charged, will do work in lifting 100 pounds until its "soul" has been discharged. Still the battery has lost none of its fifty pounds. Why and how?

There is no end to questions like these revealing that we are compelled to accept many things contrary to reason and law as we understand them.

Actually, however, an evolutionist proclaims his faith in the most amazing miracle, and yet can suggest no power or method that could possibly perform them. We do believe in miracles and we have a miracle-working God. "He spake and it was done, He commanded and it stood fast."

That certain Laws operate in the universe is obvious. Behind the law must be a Law-Giver. We observe plan and design everywhere requiring a designing Intelligence to bring them into action. To persist in affirming that no God is needed to account for the intricate and exact operations of Nature is to deny the irresistible logic of our reasoning faculties. A multitude of great scientists have thus been compelled to admit the existence of a Supreme Personality. There is no other adequate solution that will satisfy our mind's questioning.

Dr. Robert A. Millikan wrote in "The Commentator," June, 1937:

"Every one who reflects at all believes . . .
in God . . . To me it is unthinkable that a
real atheist should exist at all. . . . If you,
in your conception, identify God with Nature you must attribute to Him consciousness and personality, or better, supercon-
sciousness and super-personality. You cannot possibly synthesize nature and leave
out of it its most outstanding attributes.
Nor can you get these potentialities out of
Nature no matter how far back you go in
time. In other words, materialism, as commonly understood, is an altogether absurd
and utterly irrational philosophy, and is so
regarded, I believe, by most thoughtful
men."

This affirmation of faith by Dr. Millikan is important. Many other scientists hold the same opinion, but
it must be granted that they are in the minority. There
is not the same gross materialism which was so vocal
twenty-five years ago, but everywhere there is hesi-
tancy in admitting what seems to be obvious—namely,
that all the proven facts of Science indicate the necessity of a supreme Creator. This Creator must have
Personality. In other words, the Bible antedated by
many centuries this great discovery.

In spite of this corroboration offered by a reluctant
modern science to the accuracy of the Scriptural description of the God of the universe, the current references to Him are extremely hazy and indefinite. Why
should this be? The answer is not hard to find. If there
is a God such as the Bible writes about, then follow
other inescapable implications. For instance, this personal God possessed of Omniscience and Omnipotence

must have had the ability to transmit to us His revelation regarding His purpose in the creation of man, including the startling truth of man's fall, and God's plan of redemption.

This revealed plan involves not only recognition of the existence of God, but it necessitates a surrendered will to Jesus Christ, God's Son, the divine Substitute for mankind, who died on behalf of doomed humanity, sentenced because of sin to eternal death.

And more than this, God's Word says there is no other way to eternal bliss than this one way, via faith in the Son of God and submission to Him in all things which constitute our daily living.

And here is where the difficulty lies. Jeremiah tells us that "the human heart is deceitful above all things and desperately wicked." This tremendous fact is hardly realized until we are face to face with the necessity of making a decision which involves the acceptance of a righteous Saviour and a change of life habits. It is then we discover that all our natural tendencies are evil.

Natural man is at enmity with God, and finding he has the power to defy God without any immediate result, decides that he may continue this attitude and in some way more pleasing to himself and apart from God ultimately get to heaven.

As God is real and personal, so is the Devil. This great enemy of God is a religious enthusiast. It is commonly thought that he specializes in making men immoral and debased, so that they become bestial and depraved, ending their career in the gutter. This current idea is far from being true.

What the Devil desires and labors ceaselessly to secure is a host of followers who will be outwardly as moral and excellent as the true disciples of Christ but who will refuse to acknowledge the claims of Christ. Thus, Satan sets himself up in opposition to God and builds for himself a wide-spread kingdom as he attempts to dethrone the Creator God. He appeals to the pride of man and declares that man has in himself that spark of divinity which is the same as that possessed by Christ. He urges us to remain "masters of our fate." He argues that it is humiliating to think we must place ourselves in the power of another—even God.

That this is a very potent and persuasive line of reasoning is easily seen. It agrees with our natural inclinations and enables us to enjoy pride of accomplishment and discovery without any abject surrender of our wills and selfish desires.

And so, our great men of the world, for the most part, turn away from the acknowledgment of God, preferring as they think, to maintain control of their wills. In reality, they have become slaves to God's archenemy.

May I make this matter personal? Every one is slave to God or to the Devil. Who is YOUR Master, my friend? It is a glorious privilege to line up with God, thus making sure of eternity, and for the present knowing the blessedness of the man who fellowships with God. Thus we meet the future not only unafraid but with the sure expectation of glory that will never end. What will you do about it?

Let me say again that the Lord Jesus is a wonderful Saviour.

CHAPTER XXXVI

WINGED WONDERS

Today we begin our study of Birds and their ways. Birds are of very special interest because they exhibit remarkable and well-established instincts, combined with what would seem to be intelligence. Many birds are quick to learn new ways, and it is impossible for us to explain some of their astonishing performances.

Any animal which has a covering of feathers belongs to the Bird class. They are feathered bipeds, they are warm-blooded, and they lay eggs. Warm-blooded means that they keep the same body temperature day and night, summer and winter, the only other warm-blooded animals being the Mammals to which we have just been giving our attention.

There are five running birds with undeveloped wings: the African Ostrich, the American Ostrich, the Emu, the Cassowary, and the Kiwi; all others have the power of flight, except in rare cases like the Penguins of the Antarctic.

Birds are endowed with two widely open gateways of knowledge—the sense of sight and the sense of hearing. You have watched gulls pick up pieces of biscuit from the foam in the wake of a steamer. Not less striking is the keen way in which a hawk scrutinizes a hillside in search of young birds and mammals. From a great height it detects a victim and descends like a bolt from the blue. Vultures gather to a carcass by sight rather than by smell.

One vulture sees the animal stagger and fall, and descends on it. A second follows the first, and a third the second; so the news spreads through the sky.

Longfellow, in one of his poems, uses this picture to illustrate the way in which misfortunes often follow one another:

> "Never stoops the soaring vulture on his
>   quarry in the desert,
> On the sick and wounded bison, but an-
>   other vulture watching
> From his high aerial look-out, sees the
>   downward plunge and follows,
> And a third pursues the second, coming
>   from the invisible ether,
> First a speck and then a vulture, till the air
>   is thick with pinions.
> So disasters come not singly."

In addition to this keen sense of sight, birds have an equally sharp sense of hearing. The breaking of a twig is enough to send the bird off at full speed, or to make it utter the danger-signal. To those young birds hatched at an advanced stage, and able to run about almost immediately, the quick ear means much. These newborn birds come into life endowed with an instinctive appreciation of a particular warning-cry which their parents utter. Whenever they hear it, they crouch and lie motionless.

Thus in the case of partridges, the parents make a peculiar cluck-clucking note, and the young birds squat flat, remaining absolutely still. They will do this when only two or three hours old. Yet, if reared by a foster-mother hen, they pay no attention to what she says, no matter how much anxiety she puts into her call.

What is the meaning of this? Their nervous and muscular systems are obviously adjusted from the beginning, before birth, to answer one particular call. Their unfailing obedience to this parental call does not mean that they have any understanding of what they are doing when they lie motionless. Their lives depend on this sense. They could not have developed it gradually through the centuries. They could not survive in the first place without having this equipment. That means, it was CREATED, not evolved.

The sense of touch in birds does not seem to be acute, except in the bills of those birds that feel their food before or without seeing it. Thus the woodcock probes for earthworms in the moist soil of the wood, and the tip of its bill has a fine equipment of nerve-endings. The snipe also feels for food which it does not see.

Taste is not greatly developed in birds, for they are much given to bolting their food and hurrying on. However, chickens will soon learn to avoid unpalatable caterpillars, and hungry ducklings, after one trial, will refuse tiny foreign frogs with poisonous skins.

Little is known of the sense of smell in birds, and this is true also of the other senses, temperature and pressure and balance. Migrating birds must surely be possessed of a sense unknown to us, making their way accurately for thousands of miles, steering an unerring course by day and by night.

If a boy could ride a bicycle at the first attempt, that would be an inborn or instinctive aptitude. Birds show much of this gift. For instance, young water birds, when tumbled into the water, swim at once. In some cliff birds, where the birthplace may be a ledge two or three hundred feet above the sea, as with the razor-bills, the parents have to coax or even force the young bird to take the first plunge. Sometimes they help down the young bird, and even seem to give actual instruction. Thus, the mother Great Crested Grebe takes her young ones on her back for a sail, and then, sinking beneath the water, leaves them gently afloat.

Besides learning the art of swimming quickly, the same is generally true of flying and diving, pecking and scratching, crouching and lying low. But we soon come to the end of the list and then find the young bird actually learning.

Professor Lloyd Morgan observed that his chicks, hatched out in the laboratory away from any bird, paid no attention to their own mother's cluck when she was brought outside the door. Later on, when they were thirsty, and willing to drink from a moist finger-tip, they did not know what water was for, even when they walked through a saucerful. It was only when they happened to peck their toes when standing in the dish that they appreciated water as the thing they wanted. Only then, did they raise their bills to the sky in the familiar fashion. Later on, these unprejudiced youngsters stuffed their crops with red yarn, as if they mistook the pieces for worms. Evidently they missed their mother's teaching, but they soon learned. Not more than once or twice did they try the red worsted or the unpalatable caterpillar. They learned with great rapidity.

Diving birds will swim away at once after birth, but it may be weeks before they know they can dive. A bird seems to need something to arouse the diving instinct, such as a dog running down the bank, barking. Without a second's hesitation the bird will disappear under the water for the first time in its life, remaining under for sometime and then peeping carefully, its head just showing above water. Nothing had previously awakened the diving instinct; it was the dog's bark that pulled the trigger. Intelligence and instinct joined hands and the power which was present at birth was now available when needed. Creation again!

The song-thrush knows how to break snail shells on a stone anvil. Miss Frances Pitt, in her Wild Creatures of Garden and Hedgerow, tells of this curious habit. To a young thrush which she had brought up by hand, she offered some wood-snails, but he took no interest in them until one of the snails put out its head and began to move. The bird then pecked at its horns and seemed amazed when the snail retreated within the shelter of its shell. This happened over and over again, the bird's inquisitiveness increasing day by day. The thrush often picked up a shell by the lip and let it fall, but no real progress was made until the sixth day, when the bird seized the snail and beat it on the ground somewhat in the same manner as thrushes do with a big earthworm. At last on the same day, he picked up a snail, and hit the shell repeatedly against a stone. He tried one snail's shell after another. After fifteen minutes of hard work, he managed to break one. After that, it was easy. A tendency to beat things seems to be inborn in this bird, but in this particular instance, he seemed to have learned intelligently how to solve a fairly difficult problem.

Birds, like any backboned animals, often show quickness in forming a connection between some sight or sound and an appropriate action. Professor Morgan tells of a moor-hen chick for whom he used to dig earthworms. This bird soon learned to run to him from some distance whenever he took the spade in hand. It is not necessary to suppose that the bird reasoned,

"He's got hold of the thing that brings me worms," but some association evidently existed in the bird's mind between the spade and a pleasant hunger-satisfying experience.

All of us have watched birds collecting food and dealing with it. We have gazed at the robin on the lawn, hopping here and there, cocking its head on one side, listening intently, and then making a quick thrust to bring out an earthworm without breaking it, and leaning back to stretch the worm for careful removal. The robin has, apparently, an astonishingly acute sense of hearing, probably able to detect the slight movement of the worm below ground. Then, we have watched robins build nests and rear their young ones, and all of us have remarked with wonderment at what we have seen. These inborn gifts, or promptings, or abilities—whatever you like to call them—are instinctive. I am sure we shall enjoy a little closer examination of some of these wonders, such as nest-making, the laying of eggs and their hatching. We shall look at their feathers, their plumage and their ability to fly. Here are the operations of amazing interest from which we shall draw some conclusions of importance.

Birds are mentioned many times in the Bible as objects of God's care. I read in Luke 12:24:

> "Consider the ravens: for they neither sow
> nor reap; which neither have storehouse
> nor barn; AND GOD FEEDETH THEM;
> how much more are ye better than the
> fowls?"

Jesus compared Himself and His love and care for Jerusalem to the solicitude of a mother hen for her young. In Matt. 23:37, he speaks: "O Jerusalem, Jerusalem, . . . how often would I have gathered thy children together, even as a hen gathereth her chickens under her wings and ye would not."

In Isaiah 40:31, we are told that "they that wait upon the Lord shall renew their strength; they shall mount up with wings as eagles; they shall run and not be weary; and they shall walk and not faint."

Have we begun to learn the lesson of God's providential care of His children? It is true, of course, that only those who have the position of children of God have any right to pray for blessing. It is common to hear God called "Father," as if every person on earth came under this divine care. God is Creator of all, but in the real sense, we can only call Him Father, when we join the family, and that is the truth I am stressing so many times. It is surely very worth while to put ourselves into a position where we have the right to seek and expect care and blessing of God to become evident in our lives.

It is not to be expected that an individual who pays no attention to God—possibly takes His name in vain often, and then in a moment of need, presumes to beseech God for protection, and blessing,—has any right to expect an answer. I believe that, sometimes, God actually does intervene on behalf of gross sinners, but that does not prove the right of the recipient of His love to claim it just because He is supreme Creator. Have you qualified—as a real member of God's family? Remember the way—through Christ—and there is no other name nor way. Delay is dangerous. Will you make the decision today?

CHAPTER XXXVII

NATURE'S STREAMLINED FLYERS

Before we deal with individual species of birds, it will be of interest to make some further general observations about them. As we have noticed, birds are distinguished from all other living creatures by the feathery robe which covers their bodies, and which serves the double purpose of clothing and progression.

The skeleton of a bird repays inspection. The distinctive feature in the skull of either bird or mammal lies in the jaw-bones, which in the former are quite toothless, and at their extremities are developed into horny mandibles that form the beak or bill.

The beak varies much in shape in various tribes of birds. In birds of prey it is strong, sharp, and hooked for seizing and tearing living creatures. In the fishers, it is long and pointed, for piercing the prey in the water, and bringing it to the surface. The boring birds are furnished with a long, straight, and pointed beak, with which to dig into bark in search of grubs and insects. The nut-cracking birds have a bill, short, strong, and hooked into a sharp point. The birds which grope in the mud for food are provided with broad, flat, shovel-like bills that are soft and pliable; and the seed-eating birds have a short, conical, and hard beak, especially adapted for cracking the husks of seeds.

The neck of a bird never possesses less than nine vertebrae, but in many species the neck is longer than the body, and the vertebrae are considerably more in number—the Swan, for example, boasting of no less than twenty-three.

These neck vertebrae are extremely pliable, while those of the back are fused into what is practically one bone; but the seven or eight vertebrae of the tail are movable, terminating in one bone, which is longer than any of the others.

The ribs are fixed to the spine, and are further braced by transverse processes to form a firm and un-yielding framework. The flying muscles surpass in volume all the other muscles of the body put together; and the birds that are capable of great flight possess a ridge or keel on the breast bone to afford support to the enormous muscles that work the wing. Birds like the eagle, those with sufficient endurance to cross the sea, and even the tiny humming-bird that spends nearly all its time on the wing, have well-developed keel bones; but the breastbone of the ostrich, which does not fly at all, is almost perfectly flat.

The wings of birds are very similar in construction to the arms of a man, except that there are prac-tically no wrist-bones. The upper arm-bone or humerus, and the two lower-arm bones, radius and ulna, are there; the little projecting thumb is there also, or traces of it, the metacarpal bones of the third and fourth fingers, and even a much-reduced middle finger.

The leg bones resemble those of the mammalian quadrupeds, differing, however, in their extremities. Most birds have four toes on each foot, although there are conspicuous exceptions. The leg exhibits a simple but very effective mechanism. A great tendon, con-necting with all the toes or claws, passes over the joints in such a manner that, when the leg is bent, the tendon is shortened. By this means, the weight of the perching bird, pressing on the tendon, holds it firmly on the branch, and so during roosting, the sounder the sleep of the bird, the more securely it is held on its perch. What an admirable arrangement!

Birds may be classified according to their feet. The foot of the perching birds, such as the sparrow, thrush, and robin, has three long, slender, jointed toes in front, and a short one behind. The seizers or birds of prey possess similar but stronger feet, armed with sharp, hooked talons. The foot of the climbing bird, such as the parrot and woodpecker, is furnished with two toes in front, and two behind. The scratching birds, like the common fowl and turkey, have short, thick toes, fitted with stout, blunt claws. The wading birds, as the crane and heron, are long and slender-legged for walking in the water. Most of the swimming birds, such as ducks and swans, have webbed feet; and the ostrich has only two, short, thick toes, pointing forwards, and providing a sufficiently strong support. Other running birds have three stout toes.

Everything in the construction of the bird is subordinated to procuring strength with lightness. The body is boat-shaped, or stream-lined, decreasing in circumference from the middle toward the head in one direction, and toward the tail in the other, the very best form for cleaving the air easily and with a minimum of resistance.

The bones are lighter than those in mammals, and some of them are hollow throughout. In addition to lungs there are at least nine air chambers, all connected with the hollow bones, into which the bird can force the hot, rarefied air from its lungs.

Feathers form the airiest of dresses, and are all

directed from the head toward the tail, thus offering little resistance to air. We have already discussed briefly the formation of the feather but it is important enough to repeat. A feather consists of three parts. The quill is imbedded in the skin; it is cylinderical, hollow, nearly transparent, and very light and strong. The shaft, or continuation of the quill to the tip of the feather, is sheathed with tough, glossy, horny material, which protects an elastic substance called the pith. From both sides of the shaft spring the barbs, arranged with their flat sides toward each other, and forming a point toward the tip. To the sides of the barbs are attached numerous slender, tapering processes, termed barbules, which are really little hooks or locks holding the barbs together.

Roughly, the feathers are of three kinds. There are the clothing feathers, beautifully arranged to overlap each other, to form a closely fitting garb; the long quill feathers in the wings and tail, used for flight; and next to the skin, soft, fluffy feathers called "down," providing a warm under-jacket to protect its wearer against the cold. This downy covering retains the heat of the body of the bird, just as the blanket of blubber defends the whale from the cold icy water.

The wing expanse of every flying bird is very great in comparison with the body, and the wing muscles are powerfully developed to drive the creature through space. There is a remarkable device in the wing structure. On the stroke, the flat side of the feathers strikes the air, but there is an immediate change in position so that the sharp edge meets the air as the wing returns for the next stroke. This is the same principle adopted by the oarsman as he "feathers" the oars.

Birds "moult" their feathers twice and sometimes oftener in a year, usually immediately following the breeding season. Thus they obtain a new set of plumes to replace those which have deteriorated by wear and tear. A broken or damaged feather may be replaced at any season.

The showiest feathers are usually worn by the male birds and they take great pride in showing off their beauty during the courting season. The members of the human race have no such adornment and are compelled to use other powers to present their claims to the opposite sex.

The sight of birds shows remarkable telescopic adaptability for near or distant objects. The swallow, darting swiftly through the air, is able to see the tiniest of insects as it swoops down through the sky. A bird of prey, even at high altitude, can perceive a small object far below and in its lightning descent calculates the distance so precisely as to snatch its prey without any crash landing. The focus of the eye changes rapidly and accurately during the swift descent.

Birds, of course, produce their young from eggs which have to be kept constantly warm. It is an amazing sight to watch the gradual development of a living creature from the apparently lifeless substances within the hard calcareous shell of the egg. The "white" and the "yolk" require no description, but it is in the latter from which will come the finished bird. In the common fowl the time needed is three weeks; in other species of birds the time of hatching varies from ten days to as many weeks.

As we watch this yolk after a few hours of warmth, we notice a whitish streak, barely one-tenth of an inch long. This enlarges into two small ridges connected by a delicate thread, the first indication of the spinal cord. This is quickly followed by very tiny, square, white plates which are the beginnings of the back bone. On the second day a little heart is forming, and on the third, blood vessels appear. The various organs are gradually built up, the feathers appearing on the twelfth day. On the nineteenth and twentieth day the chick pierces a tiny air-sac at the blunt end of the egg. Because it can get this small amount of air, it is able to chirp before it chips its way out of the shell. For breaking open its shell, a hard flinty cover for its bill is provided, and is discarded shortly after birth. Is this chance or design? It is useless to ask the question, do you not think?

I will not go into the details of anatomical construction of the bird's larynx, of peculiar formation, but simply tell you that the form and movements of the apparatus permit remarkable modifications of tone. The provision of air cells, in addition to the lungs, contributes to the astonishing volume of sound some birds can produce.

We are all interested in the lovely song of birds. A caged canary, confined in a narrow space and cut off from all its kind, puts us to shame with its happy melodious song. No matter how depressing the circumstances, it seems never to be discouraged. They are thankful for whatever blessings they enjoy. They love their children and will defend them to the death. I will never forget watching spell-bound, for one quick instant, a mother canary stand bravely in the cage before an attacking cat, the baby bird shivering behind her, while the cat snatched the faithful mother with its paw and killed it before I could intervene.

Our Lord said: "Greater love hath no man than this, that a man lay down his life for his friends." A mother-bird will protect her young and sacrifice herself willingly in doing it. Do we think less of her for this display of affection? Of course not.

Well, Jesus Christ once said to His disciples: "I lay down my life, that I might take it again. No man taketh it from me, but I lay it down of myself."

Here was the supreme sacrifice of the ages—God voluntarily giving up His life. And we are sometimes told that His enemies ganged up on Him and He was unable to save Himself. In the light of many Scriptures, this notion is seen to be impossible. He came to earth to die as a Substitute for man. He died "in our room and stead," we are told. We ask why, and the answer comes ringing down through the ages:

> "For God sent not His Son into the world
> to condemn the world; but that the world
> through Him might be saved."

People are often irked by hearing that word—salvation. Call it what you will—eternal life, heaven, infinite, never-ending happiness. It comes because He took our place and removed the guilt and power of sin. Have you linked up with Him?

CHAPTER XXXVIII

TALKING BIRDS

No phase of animal life is more interesting than that of the migration of birds, many of which travel enormous distances according to season. Various mammals promptly hibernate when cold weather cuts off their natural supply of food, whereas birds simply visit another region in search of it.

In the northern hemisphere, migration toward the north is always for the purpose of finding the most suitable temperature for breeding; movement southward is always prompted by the desire for food and warmth. In later talks this subject will be dealt with as we speak of individual birds.

There are at least ten thousand species of birds, but ornithologists differ considerably regarding classification, and some authorities place the number at thirteen thousand. I can deal with but a few kinds of birds and for our first selection, we think of a very familiar class —the Crows, belonging to the family Corvidae. It is claimed for the birds of this family that they stand at the very head of the whole class Aves. It is generally agreed that the cleverest birds are rooks and parrots— the rooks having many close relatives, the common crow, the raven, magpie, jay, nutcracker, and the common chough.

In February the story of the rook begins, for that is the time of courting. The cock-bird struts and bows before the hen, and spreads out his wings and tail, attempting sometimes to sing in the gayety of his heart, but with no great success. This strutting and bowing and "singing" may occur at other seasons, when they are well pleased with themselves, but it is most marked during the courtship. An interesting little ceremony is sometimes seen. The male bird brings his desired mate a little gift—some tidbit of food, which she accepts with thanks, if she likes him. Humans haven't anything on the rooks when it comes to love-making! And in one marked respect they set us an example. Two crows remain together for life, but every year there is a period of courting.

Among the crows we find the most perfect type of wing, and the foot also is very highly developed. The Raven, the largest of the Crows, is twenty-five inches in length with a wing-spread of four feet. Its plumage is black with purple reflections.

Early in March, while the weather is still cool, the rooks begin to prepare a nest. Sometimes they use an old one over again after a thorough spring-cleaning. There is a good deal of disputing over the twigs, and up to a certain stage they steal from one another if they can. But one bird usually mounts guard while the other breaks the twigs from the leafless trees. After a while they exchange duties.

To these pliable twigs they add some earth and clay, and the inside of the nest is made comfortable with grass and leaves, hair and wool. There are often a dozen nests on one tree, and as many as thirty have been counted. If a branch breaks off, or even if there is a hint of such an accident, the crows leave the tree. They go back at night during this nest-building time to their roosting place which is usually quite apart from the rookery. When the egg-laying begins they cease traveling to and fro, to remain in the one place.

There are usually three to five eggs in one nest, and the mother bird sits very close, the male taking a turn now and then. The color of the eggs in one clutch is often different from the color in another, probably due to diet. The nests are quite conspicuous but seem to be safe from most enemies although the carrion-crows are successful robbers of nests. The common crows are not very good fighters and it may be that this softness in their character accounts for their sociability.

After the eggs hatch, the parents are kept very busy satisfying the large appetite of the youngsters. They are fed on grubs and wireworms and other insects. When the newly hatched birds are very young, father hands over his collection of food to the mother, who does the actual feeding. But, later on father is permitted to feed also.

There is great excitement when the young rooks leave the nest and make their first aerial excursions. Then they indulge in various kinds of play, gambols, shamfights, and wild chases. In September there is a flitting from the rookery to the roosting place, where they spend the winter, or sometimes there may be a partial migration to more congenial quarters.

I am speaking of rooks and crows as if they were identical. Technically, this is not quite true. There is a slight difference in the form of the beak. In the rook the base of the beak is destitute of feathers, and covered with a white scurf. And also, the rooks are even more sociable than the crows which usually live together in pairs, while the rooks love a communal life near humans. But for the purposes of this practical study we may consider them together.

This family of birds are great talkers, and seem to have quite a number of sounds or "words"—to use that term in this connection—which they themselves understand. It is quite an exciting experience to get into a large rookery where they all seem to be talking at once —almost as interesting as a sewing bee at Brown's Corners!

Almost all members of the Parrot family are very social birds and given to much conversation. Most of them are tropical and have very clear-cut characters, so that everyone knows a parrot at first glance. However, some love-birds are hardly larger than sparrows, and the great macaws are three feet long. The outstanding feature, of course, is the shape of the beak which is short and strongly hooked, the upper hinged mandible hanging far over the lower one. This hooked apparatus is used skilfully to assist in climbing. The tongue is short, thick, and fleshy; the wings and tail are generally long.

The first and fourth toes are turned backward, the second and third forward, thus giving them a good grip of branches. Most of them have a brilliant plumage and many of them are startling. In some kinds, the males are green and the females red. Most parrots have a harsh voice, but a remarkable imitative power which varies with the kind and the individual, and bears some relation to cleverness. What parrots say often suggests keener wits than they actually possess. Trained to utter words and sentences that are particularly to the point in certain situations, they often surprise us.

A grey parrot belonging to an English lady living in Florida showed a keen sense of humor. There were three dogs on the place. The parrot, quite on his own account, learned the various whistles which would call these dogs, and would utter each in turn, as if they belonged to three different owners. The dogs would come racing up to the verandah where the parrot's cage hung, causing the bird to fling up its head and utter shrieks of laughter, while the disappointed dogs slunk away. The parrot was careful not to try the trick too often, not more than once or twice daily.

They lay two or three white eggs in the holes of trees. Parakeets, which are much smaller than parrots, sometimes lay a dozen eggs.

Of the true Parrots, there is no better example than the Grey Parrot which ranges across Africa. This short-tailed Parrot is almost wholly ashen grey, except the tail which is a deep scarlet. It has an astonishing power of imitating all kinds of sounds. One of these Grey Parrots repeated faithfully all the sounds emitted by a dog, which was run over in the street. First, the sudden, half frightened bark, as danger threatened; then the loud shriek of pain as the wheel struck; followed by a series of howls as the dog limped away and turned the corner in the distance. The bird's performance reveals a tenacious memory and keen powers of observation.

It can copy the human voice and carry in its memory quite a stock of words. It is one of the hardiest of cage birds and not uncommonly lives to the age of seventy or more years.

In our somewhat random sampling of bird life, the Cuckoo, ally of the Woodpecker, deserves at least a brief mention. This bird is a parasite. And the most remarkable circumstance connected with its life-history is the habit of depositing its eggs in the nests of other birds, leaving to them the care of its offspring. This seems to be an ingenious labor-saving device, which certainly should not be generally followed!

This feathered interloper has been known to select the nests of almost one hundred and fifty species, imposing equally on small and larger birds. In all probability the nest selected resembles the one in which the cuckoo itself was reared. During the season, this vagrant may lay from five to twenty eggs. These vary in color, but are usually greyish green or reddish grey.

The young Cuckoo is an ungrateful little tyrant. With its shovelshaped back it pushes out eggs and nestlings, and forthwith monopolizes the fullest attention of the devoted and very much cheated foster parents.

The Cuckoo is a migratory bird and will travel between Africa and England. The old birds start south in July and August, leaving their family behind, since they are not yet strong enough for the long journey. Yet, a little later the young birds unerringly wing their way in the track of their vagrant parents.

In my next talk, I think I shall digress somewhat in order to discuss one of the most remarkable habits of birds—that is, the nesting, and the laying, and hatching of eggs. Here is a wonder that has never been explained and may well occupy our attention. I shall ask some interesting questions.

Inevitability our minds are asking — "How did the birds originate in their varied forms, with their different habits, and capabilities, and appearance, yet all of them having feathers as a covering, frequently of striking beauty and cleverness?" I read the considered judgment of one emiment scientist. He writes: "Birds sprang from reptilian ancestors, active, high-strung,

SCALY creatures, that ran swiftly along the ground, and took running leaps on to the lower branches of trees."

To me, it seems a far cry from scaly reptiles to feathered birds. How did scales change to feathers? How did wings arise? How did it happen that the wings are in exactly the right position for flying? Did the reptiles call a convention and decide to lighten their body and take to the air? How long did this operation take? Did it last more than the lifetime of one generation of birds? How did succeeding generations find out what had been planned and carried out? How COULD this possibly be?

How much more simple and logical to accept the explanation of Gen. 1:20, 21: "And God said . . . let fowl fly above the earth in the open firmament of heaven. And God created every winged fowl after its kind: and God saw that it was good."

Friends, that satisfies me completely. I ask you not to be fooled by any glib assertions, wholly unsupported by evidence, that these lovely forms of animated life came by chance from a repulsive reptile. Our God is a God of superlative artistry and infinite wisdom and power. Can anyone deny the evidence of the facts and say there is no God? Yes—as I read in Psalm 14: "The fool hath said in his heart, There is no God." But who wants to be a fool? Will you let God into your life today?

CHAPTER XXXIX

THE STRANGE JOB OF LAYING EGGS

In my last talk I told you that today I would consider the nesting of birds, egg-laying, and hatching. These features are, obviously, wrapped up with the question of instinct which is seen in all these animals.

An instinct, then, is some tendency, innate in character, prior to experience, and quite independent of instruction. It is only by instinct the different sexes of animals seek each other; that animals cherish their offspring; that the young quadruped is directed to the teat of its mother; that birds build their nests, and brood with so much patience upon their eggs; that insects which do not sit upon their eggs, deposit them in those particular situations, in which the young, when hatched, find their appropriate food; that the salmon, and some other fish, travel out of the sea into rivers for the purpose of spawning in fresh water.

Out of all this catalogue, none is more interesting than the incubation of eggs. Two sparrows, for instance, hatched in an incubator, and kept separated from the rest of their species, proceed as other sparrows do in everything related to the producton and preservation of their brood. The constant question—HOW?—is ever on our lips. The only answer is inborn created instinct.

What could induce the female bird to prepare a nest before she lays her eggs? It is vain to suppose that she is possessed of the faculty of reasoning; no reasoning will satisfy the case.

The fullness or distension which she may feel in a particular part of her body, because of the growth and solid character of the egg within, could not possibly inform her that she was about to produce something of great importance—something which, when produced, must be preserved with great care. She has had no experience which could lead to this inference, or to this suspicion. In fact, everything is against it. In every other instance, what issues from her body is cast out and rejected.

Let us suppose the egg is laid. How should birds know that their eggs contain their young? There is nothing, either in the external appearance or internal composition of an egg which could lead even the most daring imagination to conjecture that, after a time from inside the shell, will come a perfect bird.

The form of the egg bears not the slightest resemblance to that of a bird. If we, knowing nothing about the wonder, examined the shell and its contents, how could WE guess that they might be designed for the abode and nutrition of an animal? We might conceivably look for some kind of a slimy tadpole to come forth, but never a dry, winged, feathered creature. The contents of the egg examined prior to hatching bear no imaginable relation to that which comes out of it.

From the white of an egg, would any one ever look for the feathers of a goldfinch? Who would expect, from this homogeneous substance, to come the most complicated of all machines, a perfect body of skin and feathers, bones, tissues, and organs, all working harmoniously, able to perform the most complex physiological operations easily and without cessation?

Nor would the process of incubation lead us to expect the event. Who, seeing the faint streaks beginning to form in the yolk would imagine that these were soon to become bones and limbs? Who, that spied the minute pulsating point which appears two days after incubation, could anticipate that it would soon become the heart, the center of a complete circulatory mechanism?

For the sake of the argument, let us suppose that the sparrow, manifesting exceeding intelligence, had discovered that within that egg was concealed the principle of a future bird. Are we to suppose further, that she had been taught by some famous bird professor, who had assured her that warmth was necessary to bring the egg to maturity? And did he inform her that the warmth of her body would supply the heat in just the right degree?

No, this mother sparrow is not possessed of that sagacity and reason to enable her to arrive at such astonishing conclusions. There are no premises to justify such an expectation. If she had this knowledge, she must have penetrated into the order of nature further than any human faculties have yet gone.

But with all her apparent cleverness she seems to combine great stupidity. The hen will mistake a piece of chalk for an egg; she never misses any eggs if removed, nor pays any attention if more are added; she does not distinguish between her own and those of another species, as we saw with the cuckoo; she is very frightened, if having hatched out duck-eggs, her breed of ducklings take to the water.

Young birds just hatched and taken out of their nests to a cage, thus removed from all associations with their kind and deprived of all possible means of instruction, will yet build their nests in the same manner as in the wild state, and sit on their eggs. Must we believe that in the first few minutes after hatching, mother bird whispered a full account of everything to her very young child, and baby bird was able to understand and store away for future use all this valuable information?

The hen shows her dumbness in sitting faithfully upon non-fertile eggs, in the laying of which there has been no communication with the male bird. Too bad that she was not let into this secret, too! If incubation had been the subject of instruction or tradition, this important item would never have been overlooked—important, that is, to domesticated fowls. Non-fertile eggs are not found in wild life.

To what conclusion in regard to the origin of birds are we driven by this remarkable fact of instinct? There is but one explanation and it is not gradual development through the ages. It is Creation. As I have pointed out many times, these instincts are necessary for the life of the individual and for the propogation of the species. To be of use they must be perfect; an imperfect instance would result in the death of the animal. Consequently, it could not have been evolved or developed through thousands of years from a small, imperfect beginning to its present perfect state. The only possible and logical explanation is that the first birds that appeared on earth found themselves fully equipped to do certain things, and to do them unconsciously and without any particular thought or plan. From what source could this gift come? Only one Source—God.

I ask you—is there anything wrong with my argument? If so let me know where the logic is faulty. No one has yet been able to offer any solution, apart from creation. Think of it another way. Suppose we say instinct has been as gradually developed. Then, how long did the animals live without these instincts? Every one knows they are essential to their continued life now. Imagine a bird, if you can, without any power to lay eggs, no knowledge of any of the intricacies of hatching and rearing young. She feels lonely; she would like some small children; how shall she get them? Can we by any stretch of a credulous imagination suppose that by thinking hard she was able to devise the plan of forming an egg inside her body, this egg required to take all the other difficult steps necessary for its structure, growth, birth and rearing?

Did she plan that the baby bird should have a tiny stiff cover for its beak with which to cut its way through the shell, and then toss the beak cover away because not required any further? It is too much for me, any way I look at it.

But with God in the picture, everything becomes easy and understandable. At least, we have a sufficient cause, even though we cannot grasp the miraculous way the cells carry out their predestined work in order to complete the predetermined form.

Why man should shy away from this truth is difficult to understand. To me, it is a thrilling, exciting and magnificent Revelation that this entire universe comes from the Omnipotent hand of an Infinite Creator. Otherwise, everything is chaos, the blackness of darkness forever. But God is light and in Him is no darkness at all. And Jesus said: "I am the Light of the World." Physical darkness is dangerous, and uncomfortable, and distressing. We go to great expense and trouble to supply ourselves with lighting facilities. That is good and reasonable.

Spiritual darkness is tremendously more dangerous. We know that the Evil One prefers darkness rather
than light because his deeds are evil. None of our
scientists can supply us with SPIRITUAL light; it de-
fies manufacture. It cannot be purchased, but it CAN
be secured as a free gift. Any seeking person—man,
woman, child—can have it without money and without
price, just for the asking. The asking, of course, must
be from the only Supplier of this precious commodity
—the Lord Jesus Christ. What about it—you who listen
to my voice?

Have you thought of yet another wonder of egg-
laying? Do you know that moth and butterflies deposit
their eggs on the precise substances, a cabbage leaf, for
example, from which, not the butterfly herself, but the
caterpillar which is to issue from her eggs, draws its
necessary food.

The butterfly cannot taste the cabbage. Cabbage is
no food for her; yet, in the cabbage, and not by chance,
but studiously and electively, she lays her eggs. There
are also willow caterpillars. But we never find upon the
willow a caterpillar which prefers cabbage; nor on the
cabbage, a caterpillar that prefers willow.

How does the butterfly know which leaf the caterpillar, which hatches from her egg, will prefer. She
was never taught because she never knew her own
caterpillar form, nor has she ever had any communication with her butterfly parent. So it all breaks down
into an absurdity. As a matter of fact the parent race
is gone before the new brood is hatched.

Can the butterfly recall her caterpillar state, its
tastes and habits? Does she know that the little round
body which drops from her abdomen will produce a
living creature, not like herself at all, but like the

worm she remembers herself once to have been? Then, having indulged in these wise reflections, does she make definite provision for an order of things which she concludes will sometime take place?

I have asked enough questions, I'm sure. It is certain they cannot be answered. God asks many questions also. He challenges us to find any cause apart from Himself for the wonders of Nature. Listen! "Who hath put wisdom in the inward parts? Or who hath given understanding to the mind? . . . Who provideth for the raven his prey when his young ones cry unto God? . . . is it by thy wisdom that the hawk soareth and stretcheth her wings toward the south? Is it at thy command that the eagle mounteth up, and maketh her nest on High . . . on the cliff she dwelleth, and maketh her home . . . she spieth out the prey; her eyes behold it afar off."

Seeing all this we say with the Psalmist: "O Lord, how manifold are Thy works; in wisdom hast Thou made them all." Do you believe it?

William Jessup University
Library
333 Sunset Blvd.
Rocklin, Ca 95765